SHURLEY ENGLISH

English Made Easy

America

This booklet belongs to:

Student Workbook Level 7

SHURLEY INSTRUCTIONAL MATERIALS, INC., CABOT, ARKANSAS

03-08
ISBN 978-1-58561-111-9 (Level 7 Student Workbook)

For additional information or to place an order, write to: Shurley Instructional Materials, Inc.
366 SIM Drive
Cabot, AR 72023

Study Skills Assessment

Name:_____ Date:_____

Directions: Rate your skills in each category by marking the appropriate column with an **X**.

GET ORGANIZED:	Excellent	Average	Needs Improvement
1. Being prepared.	☐	☐	☐
2. Organizing your desk	☐	☐	☐
3. Putting everything in its place.	☐	☐	☐
4. Realizing the importance of directions	☐	☐	☐
5. Proofreading your work.	☐	☐	☐

LISTEN:	Excellent	Average	Needs Improvement
1. Listening with your whole body	☐	☐	☐
2. Asking questions	☐	☐	☐
3. Taking notes	☐	☐	☐
4. Concentrating	☐	☐	☐
5. Listening to directions	☐	☐	☐

PLAN YOUR TIME:	Excellent	Average	Needs Improvement
1. Setting goals for yourself	☐	☐	☐
2. Planning your day	☐	☐	☐
3. Doing what is important first	☐	☐	☐
4. Making each minute count.	☐	☐	☐
5. Rewarding yourself.	☐	☐	☐

DO YOUR HOMEWORK:	Excellent	Average	Needs Improvement
1. Collecting assignments before you leave school	☐	☐	☐
2. Scheduling a time to study.	☐	☐	☐
3. Studying where you can concentrate	☐	☐	☐
4. Setting a time limit to study.	☐	☐	☐
5. Having a special place to keep homework	☐	☐	☐

If you marked any areas as "Average" or "Needs Improvement," look back at the references in those areas to help you find ways to improve. Find a study-skills partner to check your progress, to encourage you, and to give you advice and help.

SHURLEY ENGLISH

Notes: _____

_____

_____

_____

_____

_____

_____

_____

_____

_____

_____

_____

_____

_____

_____

_____

_____

_____

_____

_____

_____

_____

_____

_____

_____

_____

_____

_____

_____

_____

_____

Classroom Practice 1

Name:_____ Date:_____

SKILLS

▶ **Exercise 1:** Using Reference 8 on page 11, write the capitalization rule number in column A and the letter that best illustrates each rule in column B.

A	B	
		1. Capitalize the names of monuments.
		2. Capitalize the names of holidays.
		3. Capitalize proper adjectives.
		4. Capitalize the first, last, and important words in titles.
		5. Capitalize the first word in the topics of an outline.
		6. Capitalize the names of historical events.
		7. Capitalize the first word in the greeting of letters.
		8. Capitalize the names of political parties.
		9. Capitalize geographical regions of the country.
		10. Capitalize the days of the week and months of the year.

A. Democrats, Republicans
B. Lincoln Memorial
C. I. Sedimentary Rocks
D. Dear,
E. Revolutionary War
F. *The Trumpet of the Swan*
G. North, Midwest
H. French Restaurant
I. Saturday, September
J. Labor Day, Arbor Day

▶ **Exercise 2:** Using Reference 9 on pages 12–14, write the punctuation rule number in column A and the letter that best illustrates each rule in column B.

A	B	
		1. Use a hyphen in compound numbers.
		2. Use a period after initials.
		3. Use a colon after the salutation of a business letter.
		4. Use a comma to separate a noun of direct address.
		5. Use a comma to separate words or phrases in a series.
		6. Use a comma to set off most appositives.
		7. Use ellipsis points to show that a thought is unfinished.
		8. Use a dash to take the place of the word to in dates.
		9. Use underlining for titles of books and magazines.
		10. Use a comma to separate the city from the state.

A. Carlos, can you go?
B. Dear Mr. Johnson:
C. C.S. Lewis
D. forty-five
E. Lansing, Michigan
F. Lisa, my aunt, has retired
G. 2007–2009
H. Newsweek
I. frogs, toads, and lizards
J. If only I had...

EDITING

▶ **Exercise 3:** Write the capitalization and punctuation rule numbers for each correction in **bold**. Use References 8–9 on pages 11–14 to look up the capitalization and punctuation rule numbers.

Our boss, Mr. Hector J. Munoz, gave a speech to the employees of Tia's Foods in Austin, Texas.

▶ **Exercise 4:** Put punctuation corrections within the sentence. Write all other corrections above the sentence.
Editing Guide: Capitals: 3   Commas: 2   Misspelled Words: 1   Homonyms: 2   End Marks: 1

dan gave lynn his sister a piece of pumkin pie with wipped cream for her thanksgiving dessert

SHURLEY ENGLISH

Notes: _____

_____

_____

_____

_____

_____

_____

_____

_____

_____

_____

_____

_____

_____

_____

_____

_____

_____

_____

_____

_____

_____

_____

_____

_____

_____

_____

_____

_____

Classroom Practice 2

Name:_____ Date:_____

SKILLS

▶ **Exercise 1:** Match the definitions by writing the correct letter beside each number.

_____ 1. periods, commas, apostrophes, end marks   A. synonyms

_____ 2. words with similar meanings   B. antonyms

_____ 3. words with opposite meanings   C. homonyms

_____ 4. words that sound alike but have different meanings   D. punctuation
         and spellings

▶ **Exercise 2:** Write **a** or **an** in the blanks.

1. We saw _____ ancient crown and _____ a beautiful robe in the royal museum.

2. I tasted _____ blueberry muffin and _____ iced pastry at the new bakery on Main Street.

▶ **Exercise 3:** Identify each pair of words as synonyms or antonyms by underlining the correct answer.

1. disturb, irritate   2. permanent, temporary   3. authentic, genuine

   Synonyms or Antonyms   Synonyms or Antonyms   Synonyms or Antonyms

▶ **Exercise 4:** Underline the correct homonym in each sentence.

1. The roadrunner is a (desert, dessert) bird.   7. Ouch! I stubbed my (toe, tow) on a rock.

2. Lewis is a member of the (council, counsel).   8. Maria bought some new (close, clothes).

3. I suffered (miner, minor) injuries when I fell.   9. Will you (loan, lone) Taylor a pencil?

4. My brother plays the (base, bass) guitar.   10. Grandpa and I sat on the (peer, pier) to fish.

5. Ray was (board, bored) after an hour of sitting.   11. He slammed on the (brakes, breaks) to stop.

6. The (wait, weight) for a ticket was worth it.   12. I hope (their, there, they're) not too late.

EDITING

▶ **Exercise 5:** Correct each mistake.
    Editing Guide: End Marks: 4   Capitals: 10   Commas: 2   A/An: 1   Homonyms: 3
               Apostrophes: 1   Misspelled Words: 6

jimmy my couzin and i had neverr seen glacier national park in montana we were expecting

to sea large iceburgs and snow everywhere we were pleasently surprised too find that the park

was green inn july and had many flowers and wild animals   its an beauteful park in the sumertime

Notes: _____

_____

_____

_____

_____

_____

_____

_____

_____

_____

_____

_____

_____

_____

_____

_____

_____

_____

_____

_____

_____

_____

_____

_____

_____

_____

_____

_____

_____

_____

_____

_____

Classroom Practice 3

Name:_____ Date:_____

SKILLS

▶ **Exercise 1:** Match the definitions by writing the correct letter beside each number.

_____ 1. periods, commas, apostrophes, end marks   A. synonyms

_____ 2. words with similar meanings   B. antonyms

_____ 3. a comparison of words with similar relationships   C. analogies

_____ 4. words with opposite meanings   D. homonyms

_____ 5. words that sound alike but have different meanings   E. punctuation
          and spellings

▶ **Exercise 2:** Write either the contraction or the contraction words in the blanks.

1. they are _____   4. it's _____   7. cannot _____   10. I'll _____

2. will not _____   5. let's _____   8. could not _____   11. hadn't _____

3. do not _____   6. I've _____   9. does not _____   12. there's _____

▶ **Exercise 3:** Choose the correct missing word and put the letter in the blank.

1. **carat : carrot :: doe : ____**   a. deer   b. dough   c. bread   d. buck

2. **gym : exercise :: ____ : eat**   a. theater   b. cafeteria   c. refrigerator   d. jog

3. **shell : ____ :: husk : corn**   a. peanut   b. spell   c. cob   d. sand

▶ **Exercise 4:** Identify each pair of words as synonyms or antonyms by underlining the correct answer.

1. invent, discover   2. dreary, gloomy   3. baffle, perplex

Synonyms or Antonyms   Synonyms or Antonyms   Synonyms or Antonyms

▶ **Exercise 5:** Underline the correct homonym in each sentence.

1. Many families in the village (hall, haul) water daily.   4. Mr. Daniel has rented a (suite, sweet) at the hotel.

2. Salesmen (pedal, peddle) clothing, tools, and toys.   5. Bo told us a sorrowful (tail, tale) about Biff, his cat.

3. The (coarse, course) cloth irritated her delicate skin.   6. His (hoarse, horse) voice needed soothing drops.

EDITING

▶ **Exercise 6:** Correct each mistake.

Editing Guide: End Marks: 5   Capitals: 10   Commas: 4   A/An: 1   Homonyms: 4   Misspelled Words: 3

have you ever travelled to europe i have never been their myself however i have an frend who

will be going to paris france next munth she will get to stay fore too weeks i wish i could go to

SHURLEY ENGLISH

Notes: _____

_____

_____

_____

_____

_____

_____

_____

_____

_____

_____

_____

_____

_____

_____

_____

_____

_____

_____

_____

_____

_____

_____

_____

_____

_____

_____

_____

Classroom Practice 4

Name:_____ Date:_____

SKILLS

▶ **Exercise 1:** Write either the contraction or the contraction words in the blanks.

1. have not _____ 4. let's _____ 7. did not _____ 10. we've _____

2. you had _____ 5. aren't _____ 8. does not _____ 11. you're _____

3. do not _____ 6. we'll _____ 9. has not _____ 12. I'm _____

▶ **Exercise 2:** Choose the correct missing word and put the letter in the blank.

1. **child : children :: man : ___**	a. pan	b. men	c. boy	d. woman
2. **scales : trout :: ___ : owl**	a. fish	b. fowl	c. nest	d. feathers
3. **degree : ___ :: acre : land**	a. temperature	b. oven	c. mile	d. water
4. **variety : type :: ___**	a. knee : tree	b. debate : argue	c. ox : oxen	d. mock : honor

▶ **Exercise 3:** Identify each pair of words as synonyms or antonyms by underlining the correct answer.

1. spicy, bland
Synonyms or Antonyms

2. savage, ferocious
Synonyms or Antonyms

3. occasional, frequent
Synonyms or Antonyms

▶ **Exercise 4:** Underline the correct homonym in each sentence.

1. I am studying the (principals, principles) of law.
2. Please (pore, pour) the pancake batter carefully.
3. The horse's (gait, gate) was strong and smooth.
4. Jill bought (bridal, bridle) supplies for her wedding.
5. Which (mode, mowed) of transportation was fastest?
6. The koala ate (its, it's) leaves high in a tree.
7. (Your, You're) smoke detector is not working.
8. Juanita is (morning, mourning) her bird's death.
9. A (pain, pane) of the old window was cracked.
10. The back (stairs, stares) were narrow and steep.

EDITING

▶ **Exercise 5:** Correct each mistake.
Editing Guide: End Marks: 4   Capitals: 13   Commas: 3   Homonyms: 5   Misspelled Words: 4   Apostrophes: 1

poet robert frost was borne in san francisco however he is rememered as new englands

best pote he moved too new hampshire and unsuccessfully tried two raze chickens fortunately

for the chickens and us frost descovered his talent four poetry and gave up poltry farming

Notes: _____

_____

_____

_____

_____

_____

_____

_____

_____

_____

_____

_____

_____

_____

_____

_____

_____

_____

_____

_____

_____

_____

_____

_____

_____

_____

_____

_____

_____

Chapter 1 Checkup 5

Name:_____ Date:_____

SKILLS

▶ **Exercise 1:** Write either the contraction or the contraction words in the blanks.

1. are not _____   4. hadn't _____   7. should not _____   10. he'd _____

2. is not _____   5. won't _____   8. could've _____   11. I'll _____

3. she will _____   6. doesn't _____   9. did not _____   12. I've _____

▶ **Exercise 2:** Choose the correct missing word and put the letter in the blank.

1. **baby : bonnet :: king : ____**   a. crown   b. queen   c. ring   d. stroller

2. **cocoa : chocolate :: ____ : butter**   a. cookies   b. sputter   c. cream   d. cake

3. **Earth : ____ :: Kansas : America**   a. planet   b. USA   c. Mars   d. solar system

4. **inspect : examine :: ____**   a. boulder : rock   b. thick : thin   c. aisle : isle   d. hunt : punt

▶ **Exercise 3:** Identify each pair of words as synonyms or antonyms by underlining the correct answer.

1. business, leisure   2. inquiry, question   3. flimsy, sturdy
   Synonyms or Antonyms   Synonyms or Antonyms   Synonyms or Antonyms

▶ **Exercise 4:** Underline the correct homonym in each sentence.

1. He was thrown a life (buoy, boy) to stay afloat.
2. We watched a (cereal, serial) story on TV.
3. The toys at the discount store are (cheap, cheep).
4. He stared ahead as if he were in a (days, daze).
5. A tiny (flea, flee) hopped across the floor.
6. The exercise equipment was made of (steal, steel).
7. Dee held the (reigns, reins) tightly and rode away.
8. A black weather (vane, vein) was on top of the barn.
9. Please do not (medal, meddle) with the DVD player.
10. She wore a (plain, plane) red sweater and red pants.

EDITING

▶ **Exercise 5:** Correct each mistake.
   Editing Guide: End Marks: 4   Capitals: 14   Commas: 2   A/An: 1   Homonyms: 4
   Apostrophes: 1   Misspelled Words: 1

mom and aunt darlene my moms sister visited hoover dam on us highway 93 in nevada during

there easter vacation in april they called us fore times before they even started the tour they

sounded just like little girls making an big discovery we new they wood have a fantastick time

Notes: _____

_____

_____

_____

_____

_____

_____

_____

_____

_____

_____

_____

_____

_____

_____

_____

_____

_____

_____

_____

_____

_____

_____

_____

_____

Classroom Practice 6

Name:_____ Date:_____

GRAMMAR

▶ **Exercise 1:** Classify each sentence. Underline the complete subject once and the complete predicate twice.

1. _____ Mice scurried frantically away today.

2. _____ Squirrels chattered endlessly overhead.

3. _____ Traffic stopped rather unexpectedly yesterday.

▶ **Exercise 2:** Name the three parts of speech that you have studied so far.

1. _____   2. _____   3. _____

SKILLS

▶ **Exercise 3:** Underline the correct answer.
1. Jeanne slept soundly in a (berth, birth) on the train.
2. Mom washed everyone's bedding frequently to kill dust (mights, mites).
3. You should turn (right, rite, write) on Windsor Lane.
4. (Who's, Whose) backpack has been left on the bus?
5. Tyler had (a, an) good excuse for his absence.

▶ **Exercise 4:** Write either the contraction or the contraction words in the blanks.

1. did not _____   3. we're _____   5. will not _____   7. they'll _____
2. I have _____   4. can't _____   6. I am _____   8. you're _____

EDITING

▶ **Exercise 5:** Correct each mistake.
Editing Guide: End Marks: 5   Capitals: 8   Commas: 10   Homonyms: 1   Misspelled Words: 6

i love thanksgiving day it is the time my ants uncles and couzins get togather   we visit with

each other play games and eat food usually our thanksgiving meal includes turkey potatos

dressing cranberrys vegetables and pumpken pie thanksgiving is my favorit time of year

SHURLEY ENGLISH

Notes: _____

Classroom Practice 7

Name:_____ Date:_____

GRAMMAR

▶ **Exercise 1:** Classify each sentence. Underline the complete subject once and the complete predicate twice.

1. _____ The three enormous whales floated along very slowly.

2. _____ Several chestnut horses ran surprisingly fast.

3. _____ An extremely brilliant doctor spoke very reluctantly today.

▶ **Exercise 2:** Name the four parts of speech that you have studied so far.

1._____   2._____   3._____   4._____

SKILLS

▶ **Exercise 3:** Underline the correct answer.

1. Seventeen (nay, neigh) votes were cast during the election.
2. A blanket of (dew, do, due) covered the early morning grass.
3. A chimney swift built a nest in our chimney (flew, flu, flue).
4. The neighbor's dog lost (its, it's) collar while playing in our yard.
5. Grant taught himself to ride (a, an) unicycle.

▶ **Exercise 4:** Write either the contraction or the contraction words in the blanks.

1. has not _____   3. that's _____   5. would not _____   7. I'm _____

2. were not_____   4. you'd _____   6. does not _____   8. he'll _____

EDITING

▶ **Exercise 5:** Correct each mistake.
   Editing Guide: **End Marks: 6   Capitals: 6   Commas: 7   Homonyms: 6   A/An: 2**
   Apostrophes: 3   Misspelled Words: 4

donnie my ate-year-old brother has weird tastes he loves freid eggs but only eats the yoke once

he eight an hole jar of pickled beats his favorit food and did not even get sick i cant understand

him he doesnt like reel food like ice cream hamburgurs and onyun rings hed rather eat a apple

Notes: _____

_____

_____

_____

_____

_____

_____

_____

_____

_____

_____

_____

_____

_____

_____

_____

_____

_____

_____

_____

_____

_____

_____

_____

_____

_____

_____

_____

_____

_____

_____

_____

_____

_____

Classroom Practice 8

Name:_____ Date:_____

GRAMMAR

▶ **Exercise 1:** Classify each sentence. Underline the complete subject once and the complete predicate twice.

1. _____ A dangerous copperhead slithered silently through the tall grass.

2. _____ The exceptionally eager snowboarders watch anxiously for signs of the first snow.

3. _____ The five extremely weary hikers trudged home after a long day of hiking.

▶ **Exercise 2:** Name the five parts of speech that you have studied so far.

1. _____ 2. _____ 3. _____ 4. _____ 5. _____

SKILLS

▶ **Exercise 3:** Underline the correct answer.

1. Melinda's wedding ring was made of fourteen (carat, carrot) gold.
2. Jonathan put several logs on the fireplace (great, grate).
3. Hiking twenty-one miles in four days was quite a (feat, feet) for the young men.
4. Homemade snowflakes hung from the (ceiling, sealing) in the classroom.
5. The art store made Daniel (a, an) offer for his painting that he couldn't refuse.

▶ **Exercise 4:** Write either the contraction or the contraction words in the blanks.

1. does not _____ 3. wasn't _____ 5. there is _____ 7. weren't _____

2. you are_____ 4. what's _____ 6. we had _____ 8. you'll _____

EDITING

▶ **Exercise 5:** Correct each mistake.
  Editing Guide: **End Marks: 3   Capitals: 17   Commas: 4   A/An: 1   Homonyms: 1   Misspelled Words: 3**

george washington was an southern gentlman who lived in mount vernon virginia on the

banks of the potomac river washington was comander-in-chief of the continental forces inn the

revolutionary war   george washington the first presedent of the united states took office in 1789

Notes: _____

_____

_____

_____

_____

_____

_____

_____

_____

_____

_____

_____

_____

_____

_____

_____

_____

_____

_____

_____

_____

_____

_____

_____

_____

Classroom Practice 9

Name:_____ Date:_____

GRAMMAR

▶ **Exercise 1:** Classify each sentence. Underline the complete subject once and the complete predicate twice.

1. _____ The frightened lizard bolted quickly across the windowsill toward the potted flower.

2. _____ Those enormous billows of smoke drifted darkly across the clear blue sky.

3. _____ A swarm of enraged wasps flew angrily around the busy construction workers!

▶ **Exercise 2:** Name the five parts of speech that you have studied so far.

1. _____ 2. _____ 3. _____ 4. _____ 5. _____

▶ **Exercise 3:** Choose the part of speech for the underlined word.

1. The <u>technicians</u> filed into the room. ○verb ○noun ○adjective ○adverb ○preposition
2. Two ducklings swam <u>around</u> the pond. ○verb ○noun ○adjective ○adverb ○preposition
3. <u>War</u> veterans marched in the parade. ○verb ○noun ○adjective ○adverb ○preposition
4. The cool water flowed <u>downstream</u>. ○verb ○noun ○adjective ○adverb ○preposition

SKILLS

▶ **Exercise 4:** Put the end mark and the End Mark Flow for each kind of sentence in the blanks.
Use these words in your answers: *declarative, exclamatory, imperative, interrogative.*

1. Did the doctor examine Kyle's wound__.... _____
2. This is a major earthquake ___............ _____
3. Stand behind the safety shield ___....... _____
4. Baby raccoons are called kits___........ _____

EDITING

▶ **Exercise 5:** Correct each mistake.
Editing Guide: End Marks: 3   Capitals: 3   Commas: 1   Apostrophes: 1   Homonyms: 4   Misspelled Words: 2

clearly the engagment wring was of pour quality i urged my freind to return it to the store

for a refund harvey said he couldnt get his money back because the wring was on sail

Notes: _____

_____

_____

_____

_____

_____

_____

_____

_____

_____

_____

_____

_____

_____

_____

_____

_____

_____

_____

_____

_____

_____

_____

_____

_____

_____

_____

_____

_____

Classroom Practice 10

Name:_____ Date:_____

GRAMMAR

▶ **Exercise 1:** Classify each sentence. Underline the complete subject once and the complete predicate twice.

1. _____ The dusty road in front of the travelers stretched for miles beyond the horizon.

2. _____ The aggravated snake beside the house hissed threateningly at the barking dogs!

3. _____ Tourists from the mainland waded on the beaches of Waikiki.

▶ **Exercise 2:** Use sentence 3 above to complete the table below.

List the Noun Used	List the Noun Job	Singular or Plural	Common or Proper	Simple Subject	Simple Predicate

▶ **Exercise 3:** Underline the simple subject once and the simple predicate twice.
1. The large wooden door slammed loudly.   2. The cursor on the screen flashed quickly.

▶ **Exercise 4:** Choose the part of speech for the underlined word.
1. The <u>poor</u> orphan begged for food.   ◯verb ◯noun ◯adjective ◯adverb ◯preposition
2. Escaped convicts hid <u>in</u> the garage.   ◯verb ◯noun ◯adjective ◯adverb ◯preposition

SKILLS

▶ **Exercise 5:** Put the end mark and the End Mark Flow for each kind of sentence in the blanks.
Use these words in your answers: *declarative, exclamatory, imperative, interrogative.*

1. Did the commotion in the hall disturb you ___ . . _____

2. A huge tornado is headed this way ___ . . . . _____

EDITING

▶ **Exercise 6:** Correct each mistake.
**Editing Guide: End Marks: 4   Capitals: 8   Commas: 2   Apostrophes: 2   Homonyms: 2
A/An: 2   Misspelled Words: 5**

lets have a pitza party tonight well sea if amy sarah and taylor can join us we can get an

free pizza if we order an large won at the reglar prise my faverite kind is canadian bacan

SHURLEY ENGLISH

Notes:

Chapter 2 Checkup 11

Name:_____ Date:_____

GRAMMAR

▶ **Exercise 1:** Classify each sentence. Underline the complete subject once and the complete predicate twice.

1. _____ The abandoned vehicle on the side of the road burst mysteriously into flames!

2. _____ The resourceful raccoon poked curiously through the trash at the city dump today.

▶ **Exercise 2:** Use sentence 1 above to complete the table below.

List the Noun Used	List the Noun Job	Singular or Plural	Common or Proper	Simple Subject	Simple Predicate

▶ **Exercise 3:** Underline the simple subject once and the simple predicate twice.
1. The seaworthy yacht docked in the harbor. 2. My aunt in Ohio makes delicious crescent rolls.

▶ **Exercise 4:** Choose the part of speech for the underlined word.
1. The colorful scarf hung on a hook in the hall. ☐verb ☐noun ☐adjective ☐adverb ☐preposition
2. Terrified swimmers scrambled to safety! ☐verb ☐noun ☐adjective ☐adverb ☐preposition

SKILLS

▶ **Exercise 5:** Put the end mark and the End Mark Flow for each kind of sentence in the blanks.
Use these words in your answers: *declarative, exclamatory, imperative, interrogative.*

1. Red geraniums bloomed in the window___ . . . _____

2. Apologize to the people you offended ___. . . _____

EDITING

▶ **Exercise 6:** Correct each mistake.
Editing Guide: **End Marks: 6 Capitals: 21 Commas: 1 A/An: 2 Homonyms: 2 Apostrophes: 2
Misspelled Words: 2 Underlining: 1**

the newbery medal is a award given once an year for the most distinguished contrbution to

childrens literature this award has been given since 1922 by the american library association.

in 2001 the winer was a year down yonder by richard peck another of pecks book also one the

newbery medal in 1999 how many newbery books can you name how many have you red

SHURLEY ENGLISH

Notes: _____

_____

_____

_____

_____

_____

_____

_____

_____

_____

_____

_____

_____

_____

_____

_____

_____

_____

_____

_____

_____

_____

_____

_____

_____

_____

_____

_____

_____

_____

English Made Easy

Classroom Practice 12

Name: _____ Date: _____

INDEPENDENT PRACTICE & REVISED SENTENCES

1. Write a Practice Sentence according to the labels you choose.
Use the **SN V** labels once. You may use the other labels in any order and as many times as you wish in order to make a Practice Sentence.
Chapter 2 labels for a Practice Sentence: SN, V, Adj, Adv, A, P, OP

2. Write a Revised Sentence. Use the following revision strategies: *synonym (syn)*, *antonym (ant)*, *word change (wc)*, *added word (add)*, *deleted word (delete)*, or *no change (nc)*. Under each word, write the abbreviation of the revision strategy you use.

Labels:

Practice:

Revised:

Strategies:

Labels:

Practice:

Revised:

Strategies:

Labels:

Practice:

Revised:

Strategies:

Notes: _____

_____

_____

_____

_____

_____

_____

_____

_____

_____

_____

_____

_____

_____

_____

_____

_____

_____

_____

_____

_____

_____

_____

_____

_____

_____

_____

Prewriting Map

Name:_____ Date:_____

Purpose: _____

Type of Writing: _____

Audience: _____

Topic: _____

TOPIC

1ST MAIN POINT

2ND MAIN POINT

3RD MAIN POINT

SUPPORTING DETAIL	SUPPORTING DETAIL	SUPPORTING DETAIL
SUPPORTING DETAIL	SUPPORTING DETAIL	SUPPORTING DETAIL
SUPPORTING DETAIL	SUPPORTING DETAIL	SUPPORTING DETAIL

Notes: _____

_____

_____

_____

_____

_____

_____

_____

_____

_____

_____

_____

_____

_____

_____

_____

_____

_____

_____

_____

_____

_____

_____

_____

_____

_____

_____

_____

_____

_____

Chapter 3 Writing Evaluation Guide

Name:_____ Date:_____

ROUGH DRAFT CHECK

_____ 1. Did you write your rough draft in pencil?

_____ 2. Did you write the correct headings on the first seven lines of your paper?

_____ 3. Did you use extra wide margins and skip every other line?

_____ 4. Did you write a title at the end of your rough draft?

_____ 5. Did you place your edited rough draft in your Rough Draft folder?

REVISING CHECK

_____ 6. Did you identify the purpose, type of writing, and audience?

_____ 7. Did you check for a topic, topic sentence, and sentences supporting the topic?

_____ 8. Did you check sentences for the right order, and did you combine, rearrange, or delete sentences when necessary?

_____ 9. Did you check for a variety of simple, compound, and complex sentences?

_____ 10. Did you check for any left out, repeated, or unnecessary words?

_____ 11. Did you check for the best choice of words by replacing or deleting unclear words?

_____ 12. Did you check the content for interest and creativity?

_____ 13. Did you check the voice to make sure the writing says what you want it to say?

EDITING CHECK

_____ 14. Did you indent each paragraph?

_____ 15. Did you put an end mark at the end of every sentence?

_____ 16. Did you capitalize the first word of every sentence?

_____ 17. Did you check for all other capitalization mistakes?

_____ 18. Did you check for all punctuation mistakes?
(commas, periods, apostrophes, quotation marks, underlining)

_____ 19. Did you check for misspelled words and for incorrect homonym choices?

_____ 20. Did you check for incorrect spellings of plural and possessive forms?

_____ 21. Did you check for correct construction and punctuation of your sentences?

_____ 22. Did you check for usage mistakes? *(subject/verb agreement, a/an choices, contractions, verb tenses, pronoun/antecedent agreement, pronoun cases, degrees of adjectives, double negatives, etc.)*

_____ 23. Did you put your revised and edited paper in the Rough Draft folder?

FINAL PAPER CHECK

_____ 24. Did you write the final paper in pencil?

_____ 25. Did you center the title on the top line and center your name under the title?

_____ 26. Did you skip a line before starting the writing assignment?

_____ 27. Did you single-space, use wide margins, and write the final paper neatly?

_____ 28. Did you staple your papers in this order: final paper on top, rough draft in the middle, and prewriting map on the bottom? Did you put them in the Final Paper folder?

Notes: _____

_____

_____

_____

_____

_____

_____

_____

_____

_____

_____

_____

_____

_____

_____

_____

_____

_____

_____

_____

_____

_____

_____

_____

_____

_____

_____

_____

_____

_____

_____

_____

_____

_____

Classroom Practice 13

Name:_____ Date:_____

GRAMMAR

▶ **Exercise 1:** Classify each sentence. Underline the complete subject once and the complete predicate twice.

1. _____ She trudged very slowly to her house at the end of our road.

2. _____ Grandfather searched through the attic for his old bowling trophy.

3. _____ Wait for your little sister by the bus stop after school.

▶ **Exercise 2:** Use Sentence 2 above to complete the table below.

List the Noun Used	List the Noun Job	Singular or Plural	Common or Proper	Simple Subject	Simple Predicate

▶ **Exercise 3:** Name the six parts of speech that you have studied so far.

1._____ 3._____ 5._____

2._____ 4._____ 6._____

▶ **Exercise 4:** Choose the part of speech for the underlined word.

1. <u>They</u> searched through the snowdrifts. ○verb ○noun ○adjective ○adverb ○preposition ○pronoun

2. The shield fell with a loud <u>clatter</u>. ○verb ○noun ○adjective ○adverb ○preposition ○pronoun

SKILLS

▶ **Exercise 5:** Put the end mark and the End Mark Flow for each kind of sentence in the blanks. Use these words in your answers: *declarative, exclamatory, imperative, interrogative.*

1. Will you examine these new copies ___ . . . . _____

2. Follow the map to Springfield carefully ___ . . . _____

3. I've lost my diamond engagement ring ___ . . . . . _____

4. I will vacuum the carpet tonight ___ . . . . _____

EDITING

▶ **Exercise 6:** Correct each mistake.
   Editing Guide: End Marks: 1   Capitals: 9   Commas: 3   Periods: 2   Apostrophes: 1   Misspelled Words: 2

jimmy will ship mrs bakers order to 209 mountin pkwy fort collins colorado on wednsday

Notes: _____

Classroom Practice 14

Name:_____ Date:_____

GRAMMAR

▶ **Exercise 1:** Classify each sentence. Underline the complete subject once and the complete predicate twice.

1. _____ We stopped in my hometown in North Dakota on our way to Canada.

2. _____ We waited for two hours at the airport during our flight delay.

3. _____ Stop at that roadside stand for fresh farm produce.

▶ **Exercise 2:** Use Sentence 1 above to complete the table below.

List the Noun Used	List the Noun Job	Singular or Plural	Common or Proper	Simple Subject	Simple Predicate

SKILLS

▶ **Exercise 3:** For each sentence, do three things: (1) Write the subject. (2) Write **S** and **Rule 1** if the subject is singular, or write **P** and **Rule 2** if the subject is plural. (3) Underline the correct verb.

Rule 1: A singular subject must use a singular verb form that ends in **s** or **es**: *is, was, has, does, swims, pushes.*

Rule 2: A plural subject, a compound subject, or the subject **YOU** must use a plural verb with **no s** or **es** ending: *are, were, have, do, swim, push.*

Subject	S or P	Rule
_____	_____	_____
_____	_____	_____
_____	_____	_____
_____	_____	_____
_____	_____	_____
_____	_____	_____
_____	_____	_____
_____	_____	_____

1. Talented dancers (twirl, twirls) around the stage.
2. The earthquake (is, are) causing building damage!
3. The engineers (is, are) puzzled about the error.
4. The parrot (talks, talk) nonstop at bedtime.
5. You (prepares, prepare) the green salad.
6. Florence and I (was, were) investigating a noise.
7. Grandma (collects, collect) antique teapots.
8. We (was, were) touring the military base.

EDITING

SHURLEY ENGLISH

Notes: _____

Classroom Practice 17

Name: _____   Date: _____

INDEPENDENT PRACTICE & REVISED SENTENCES

1. Write a Practice Sentence according to the labels you choose.
   Use the **SN/SP V** as your main labels. You may use the other labels in any order and as many times as you wish in order to make a Practice Sentence.
   Chapter 4 labels for a Practice Sentence: SN/SP, V, Adj, Adv, A, P, OP, PPA

2. Write a Revised Sentence. Use the following revision strategies: *synonym (syn), antonym (ant), word change (wc), added word (add), deleted word (delete), or no change (nc).* Under each word, write the abbreviation of the revision strategy you use.

Labels: _____

Practice: _____

Revised: _____

Strategies: _____

Labels: _____

Practice: _____

Revised: _____

Strategies: _____

Labels: _____

Practice: _____

Revised: _____

Strategies: _____

Notes: _____

_____

_____

_____

_____

_____

_____

_____

_____

_____

_____

_____

_____

_____

_____

_____

_____

_____

_____

_____

_____

_____

_____

_____

_____

_____

_____

Chapter 5 Writing Evaluation Guide

Name:_____ Date:_____

ROUGH DRAFT CHECK

_____ 1. Did you write your rough draft in pencil?

_____ 2. Did you write the correct headings on the first seven lines of your paper?

_____ 3. Did you use extra wide margins and skip every other line?

_____ 4. Did you write a title at the end of your rough draft?

_____ 5. Did you place your edited rough draft in your Rough Draft folder?

REVISING CHECK

_____ 6. Did you identify the purpose, type of writing, and audience?

_____ 7. Did you check for a topic, topic sentence, and sentences supporting the topic?

_____ 8. Did you check sentences for the right order, and did you combine, rearrange, or delete sentences when necessary?

_____ 9. Did you check for a variety of simple, compound, and complex sentences?

_____ 10. Did you check for any left out, repeated, or unnecessary words?

_____ 11. Did you check for the best choice of words by replacing or deleting unclear words?

_____ 12. Did you check the content for interest and creativity?

_____ 13. Did you check the voice to make sure the writing says what you want it to say?

EDITING CHECK

_____ 14. Did you indent each paragraph?

_____ 15. Did you put an end mark at the end of every sentence?

_____ 16. Did you capitalize the first word of every sentence?

_____ 17. Did you check for all other capitalization mistakes?

_____ 18. Did you check for all punctuation mistakes?
(commas, periods, apostrophes, quotation marks, underlining)

_____ 19. Did you check for misspelled words and for incorrect homonym choices?

_____ 20. Did you check for incorrect spellings of plural and possessive forms?

_____ 21. Did you check for correct construction and punctuation of your sentences?

_____ 22. Did you check for usage mistakes? (subject/verb agreement, a/an choices, contractions, verb tenses, pronoun/antecedent agreement, pronoun cases, degrees of adjectives, double negatives, etc.)

_____ 23. Did you put your revised and edited paper in the Rough Draft folder?

FINAL PAPER CHECK

_____ 24. Did you write the final paper in pencil?

_____ 25. Did you center the title on the top line and center your name under the title?

_____ 26. Did you skip a line before starting the writing assignment?

_____ 27. Did you single-space, use wide margins, and write the final paper neatly?

_____ 28. Did you staple your papers in this order: final paper on top, rough draft in the middle, and prewriting map on the bottom? Did you put them in the Final Paper folder?

Notes: _____

Chapter 5 Checkup 18

Name:_____ Date:_____

SKILLS

Read the article below and make an outline. Use References 73–77 to review outlining.

ARTICLE:

Summer Job Opportunities

This summer, why not earn some extra spending money? There are often many summer job opportunities available to young people.

Yard maintenance is one of the most popular jobs for young people. In the summer, it involves mowing lawns, weeding hard-to-reach areas, and bagging grass. Then, in the fall, yard maintenance includes raking leaves, bagging them, and hauling them away.

If you're not into yard care, you might consider babysitting, another great job for responsible young people. First, you must learn the rules of good babysitting. This includes showing up on time, finding out what is expected of you, getting parents' phone numbers in case of an emergency, and making sure the children in your care are happy and safe. If you want your business to grow, you should learn ways to advertise your babysitting service. The most reliable advertising is spread by word-of-mouth of satisfied customers. You can also hand out fliers and advertise in your local paper.

Finally, if childcare isn't a good match for your skills, maybe dog sitting is for you. Your main responsibilities will include feeding, watering, and exercising the dogs. Other responsibilities involve following the owner's special instructions and getting phone numbers for the owner and the veterinarian.

Regardless of which summer job you choose, you must be willing to devote time and energy to the task. If you do, you'll acquire not only spending money, but also valuable work experience. It's a lot of hard work, but it can also be very rewarding.

OUTLINE:

Notes: _____

_____

_____

_____

_____

_____

_____

_____

_____

_____

_____

_____

_____

_____

_____

_____

_____

_____

_____

_____

_____

_____

_____

_____

_____

_____

_____

_____

_____

_____

_____

Classroom Practice 19

Name:_____ Date:_____

GRAMMAR

▶ **Exercise 1:** Classify each sentence. Underline the complete subject once and the complete predicate twice.

1. _____ Look at the gorgeous colors and amazing beauty of that magnificent sunrise.

2. _____ She tripped on her shoelaces and fell down the stairs!

3. _____ Kate and I ate on the patio and swam in the pool during the summer party.

▶ **Exercise 2:** Use Sentence 2 above to complete the table below.

List the Noun Used	List the Noun Job	Singular or Plural	Common or Proper	Simple Subject	Simple Predicate

▶ **Exercise 3:** Name the seven parts of speech that you have studied so far.

1._____ 3._____ 5._____ 7._____

2._____ 4._____ 6._____

SKILLS

▶ **Exercise 4:** Identify each type of sentence by writing the correct label in the blank. (**Labels: S, F, SCS, SCV**)

_____ 1. Although the train had left the station.

_____ 2. A majestic eagle soared high above and nested on the rocky cliff.

_____ 3. Brownies and ice cream with sprinkles were served for dessert.

_____ 4. Dad tilled the vegetable garden and planted a row of corn.

▶ **Exercise 5:** Use a slash to separate the two complete thoughts in each run-on sentence.
Correct the run-on sentences as indicated by the labels in parentheses at the end of each sentence.

1. Joseph lives in Winston Joseph teaches French at the university. (**SCV**)

_____

2. The mechanic gave our car a tune-up his helper gave our car a tune-up. (**SCS**)

_____

EDITING

SHURLEY ENGLISH

Notes: _____

Classroom Practice 20

Name:_____ Date:_____

GRAMMAR

▶ **Exercise 1:** Classify each sentence. Underline the complete subject once and the complete predicate twice.

1. _____ Jason and I yelled loudly for help and pounded frantically on the locked door!

2. _____ He walked hurriedly down the long flight of stairs and headed immediately to his car.

▶ **Exercise 2:** Use Sentence 1 above to complete the table below.

List the Noun Used	List the Noun Job	Singular or Plural	Common or Proper	Simple Subject	Simple Predicate

▶ **Exercise 3:** Choose the part of speech for the underlined word.

1. <u>We</u> played in a meadow of bright wildflowers.   ⬭verb ⬭noun ⬭adjective ⬭adverb ⬭conjunction ⬭pronoun

2. My old dog <u>and</u> Siamese cat sleep together.   ⬭verb ⬭noun ⬭adjective ⬭adverb ⬭conjunction ⬭pronoun

SKILLS

▶ **Exercise 4:** Identify each type of sentence by writing the correct label in the blank. (**Labels: S, F, SCS, SCV, CD**)

_____ 1. Charlene accomplished her goals; furthermore, she got a promotion.

_____ 2. Despite a lengthy illness last winter, my grandmother.

_____ 3. Ms. Stanley's class visited the aquarium and stayed all day.

_____ 4. Emma and Sydney saw a green lizard in their tree house.

_____ 5. Mother scrubbed the shower with bleach, yet the mold grew back.

▶ **Exercise 5:** Use a slash to separate the two complete thoughts in each run-on sentence. Correct the run-on sentences as indicated by the labels in parentheses at the end of each sentence.

1. Jana made a list of recommendations the committee accepted several of them. (**CD, and**)

_____

2. You should leave for the meeting early you may get caught in traffic. (**CD; otherwise,**)

_____

EDITING

▶ Exercise 6: Correct each mistake.

SHURLEY ENGLISH

Notes:

Classroom Practice 21

Name:_____ Date:_____

GRAMMAR

▶ **Exercise 1:** Classify each sentence. Underline the complete subject once and the complete predicate twice.

1. _____ The young deer vaulted gracefully over the fence and raced swiftly into the woods.

2. _____ Leave promptly for the parade and festival in downtown Anaheim.

3. _____ The injured burglar limped painfully and complained loudly during his arrest.

▶ **Exercise 2:** Use Sentence 2 above to complete the table below.

List the Noun Used	List the Noun Job	Singular or Plural	Common or Proper	Simple Subject	Simple Predicate

▶ **Exercise 3:** Name the seven parts of speech that you have studied so far.

1._____ 3._____ 5._____ 7._____

2._____ 4._____ 6._____

SKILLS

▶ **Exercise 4:** Identify each type of sentence by writing the correct label in the blank. (**Labels: S, F, SCS, SCV, CD**)

_____ 1. Elliot enjoys playing chess; also, he likes listening to country music.

_____ 2. Amber and her mother parked on the upper deck of the parking garage.

_____ 3. A tiny white crab scurried across the sand and disappeared into a hole.

_____ 4. Along the rocky coastline in Maine.

_____ 5. He whispered words of comfort, and his daughter was able to sleep again.

▶ **Exercise 5:** Use a slash to separate the two complete thoughts in each run-on sentence.
Correct the run-on sentences as indicated by the labels in parentheses at the end of each sentence.

1. A lighthouse shines its bright light for ships it helps them to avoid dangerous rocks. (**CSV**)

_____

2. Daniel finished his homework early he could watch his favorite TV show. (**CD; consequently,**)

_____

EDITING

Homework 2

Complete this homework assignment.

1. Copy the sentence below. Classify the sentence, using the Question and Answer Flow, as you label each part.

——— Marty and I traveled along the beautiful coast of the Pacific during our summer vacation.

2. Use the four ways listed below to correct this run-on sentence.
Kirk worked on the website Cody helped him.

1. CD, and _____

2. CD; furthermore, _____

3. CD; _____

4. SCS _____

3. Number your paper 1–5. Identify each type of sentence by writing the correct label. (**Labels: S, F, SCS, SCV, CD**)

_____ 1. The pepperoni pizza and breadsticks arrived at our table piping hot.

_____ 2. When the security alarm buzzed in the building.

_____ 3. Samantha drew a dolphin on the poster board and cut it out.

_____ 4. Kent rode the subway into the city; however, he will ride home with Shelley.

_____ 5. Gail sang in a jazz band, and Lawrence played the electric guitar.

4. Write three compound sentences. For the first sentence, connect the two sentences with a comma and a conjunction (**and, but, or**). For the second sentence, connect the two sentences with a semicolon, connective adverb, and comma. For the third sentence, connect the two sentences with a semicolon only. Double-check each sentence for correct punctuation.

Examples:

1. Cary visited his friend at Christmas, but he stayed only a few days.

2. Cary visited his friend at Christmas; however, he stayed only a few days.

3. Cary visited his friend at Christmas; he stayed only a few days.

Chapter 6 Checkup 22

Name:_____ Date:_____

GRAMMAR

▶ **Exercise 1:** Classify each sentence. Underline the complete subject once and the complete predicate twice.

1. _____ Write in your journal for five minutes today.

2. _____ She and Wanda went to Tacoma for the fireworks display on Saturday night.

▶ **Exercise 2:** Use Sentence 2 above to complete the table below.

List the Noun Used	List the Noun Job	Singular or Plural	Common or Proper	Simple Subject	Simple Predicate

▶ **Exercise 3:** Choose the part of speech for the underlined word.

1. Waterbugs skimmed <u>and</u> danced on the pond. ○verb ○noun ○adjective ○adverb ○conjunction ○pronoun

2. The headset was not working <u>properly</u>. ○verb ○noun ○adjective ○adverb ○conjunction ○pronoun

SKILLS

▶ **Exercise 4:** Identify each type of sentence by writing the correct label in the blank. (**Labels: S, F, SCS, SCV, CD**)

_____ 1. Brightly-wrapped packages, balloons, and a birthday cake decorated the table.

_____ 2. Maria had practiced constantly on her flute, and she was awarded a music scholarship.

_____ 3. The classical pianist played for an hour and delighted the audience.

_____ 4. Molly searched carefully for her contact lens, but she could not find it.

_____ 5. A mother hippopotamus and her newborn calf.

▶ **Exercise 5:** Use a slash to separate the two complete thoughts in each run-on sentence.
Correct the run-on sentences as indicated by the labels in parentheses at the end of each sentence.

1. Lucy was very interested in Asian cooking she returned the new cookbook. (**CD; nevertheless,**)

_____

2. Juicy steaks sizzled on the grill outside they filled the air with a wonderful aroma. (**CSV**)

_____

EDITING

▶ **Exercise 6:** Correct each mistake. Editing Guide: **End Marks: 2   Capitals: 9   Commas: 2   Homonyms: 1**
A/An: 1   Misspelled Words: 4

shea stadium in new york city new york is home of the mets the seats in this remarkible

stadium can rotat around the field to tranform the bawl park to an football stadeum

Notes: _____

Classroom Practice 23

Name: _____   Date: _____

INDEPENDENT PRACTICE & REVISED SENTENCES

1. Write a Practice Sentence according to the labels you choose.

Use the **SN/SP V** as your main labels. You may use the other labels in any order and as many times as you wish in order to make a Practice Sentence.

Chapter 6 labels for a Practice Sentence: SN/SP, V, Adj, Adv, A, P, OP, PPA, C

2. Write a Revised Sentence. Use the following revision strategies: *synonym (syn), antonym (ant), word change (wc), added word (add), deleted word (delete),* or *no change (nc).* Under each word, write the abbreviation of the revision strategy you use.

Labels:

Practice:

Revised:

Strategies:

Labels:

Practice:

Revised:

Strategies:

Labels:

Practice:

Revised:

Strategies:

Notes: _____

_____

_____

_____

_____

_____

_____

_____

_____

_____

_____

_____

_____

_____

_____

_____

_____

_____

_____

_____

_____

_____

_____

_____

_____

_____

_____

_____

_____

_____

Chapter 7 Writing Evaluation Guide

Name:_____ Date:_____

ROUGH DRAFT CHECK

_____ 1. Did you write your rough draft in pencil?

_____ 2. Did you write the correct headings on the first seven lines of your paper?

_____ 3. Did you use extra wide margins and skip every other line?

_____ 4. Did you write a title at the end of your rough draft?

_____ 5. Did you place your edited rough draft in your Rough Draft folder?

REVISING CHECK

_____ 6. Did you identify the purpose, type of writing, and audience?

_____ 7. Did you check for a topic, topic sentence, and sentences supporting the topic?

_____ 8. Did you check sentences for the right order, and did you combine, rearrange, or delete sentences when necessary?

_____ 9. Did you check for a variety of simple, compound, and complex sentences?

_____ 10. Did you check for any left out, repeated, or unnecessary words?

_____ 11. Did you check for the best choice of words by replacing or deleting unclear words?

_____ 12. Did you check the content for interest and creativity?

_____ 13. Did you check the voice to make sure the writing says what you want it to say?

EDITING CHECK

_____ 14. Did you indent each paragraph?

_____ 15. Did you put an end mark at the end of every sentence?

_____ 16. Did you capitalize the first word of every sentence?

_____ 17. Did you check for all other capitalization mistakes?

_____ 18. Did you check for all punctuation mistakes?
(commas, periods, apostrophes, quotation marks, underlining)

_____ 19. Did you check for misspelled words and for incorrect homonym choices?

_____ 20. Did you check for incorrect spellings of plural and possessive forms?

_____ 21. Did you check for correct construction and punctuation of your sentences?

_____ 22. Did you check for usage mistakes? *(subject/verb agreement, a/an choices, contractions, verb tenses, pronoun/antecedent agreement, pronoun cases, degrees of adjectives, double negatives, etc.)*

_____ 23. Did you put your revised and edited paper in the Rough Draft folder?

FINAL PAPER CHECK

_____ 24. Did you write the final paper in pencil?

_____ 25. Did you center the title on the top line and center your name under the title?

_____ 26. Did you skip a line before starting the writing assignment?

_____ 27. Did you single-space, use wide margins, and write the final paper neatly?

_____ 28. Did you staple your papers in this order: final paper on top, rough draft in the middle, and prewriting map on the bottom? Did you put them in the Final Paper folder?

Notes:

Chapter 7 Checkup 24

Name:_____ Date:_____

SKILLS

Read the article below and make an outline. Use References 73–77 to review outlining.

ARTICLE:	OUTLINE:

ARTICLE:

Planting a Garden

Every spring, my family plants a garden so that we can enjoy fresh vegetables all summer. We all labor together because gardens are hard work and take a commitment from the whole family.

The first step in gardening is preparing the ground. To prepare the ground, you must till the garden spot. We till around the outside edges to mark the garden dimensions. On our first run, we do a shallow till. Next, after the soil is fairly loose, we do a deeper till. After tilling, we add the fertilizer. To protect ourselves, we wear protective gear—leather gloves and dust masks. Then, we work the fertilizer into the soil. After the fertilizer, we shape the rows to get the garden ready for planting.

The second step is planting the garden. Planting is my favorite part because I like putting seeds and plants in the ground. We sow vegetable seeds, and we also transplant other plants, such as tomatoes, peppers, cabbage, and broccoli.

The third step in gardening is tending the garden. At this point, tending the garden is very important. We weed our garden daily to keep the weeds from reclaiming the soil. We also continue to till the garden weekly throughout the growing season. Finally, we fertilize our garden monthly with an organic fertilizer.

Our family works hard to have a bountiful garden that always produces an abundance of fresh, healthy vegetables. I can proudly say that our garden is the envy of the neighborhood.

Notes: _____

_____

_____

_____

_____

_____

_____

_____

_____

_____

_____

_____

_____

_____

_____

_____

_____

_____

_____

_____

_____

_____

_____

_____

_____

_____

_____

_____

_____

_____

_____

_____

_____

Classroom Practice 25

Name:_____ Date:_____

GRAMMAR

▶ **Exercise 1:** Classify each sentence.

1. _____ Today, my meal did not come with fries and a drink.

2. _____ The navy pilot suddenly ejected from the burning plane!

3. _____ The tired mechanic was looking under the hood of the last car in his shop.

▶ **Exercise 2:** Use Sentence 1 above to complete the table below.

List the Noun Used	List the Noun Job	Singular or Plural	Common or Proper	Simple Subject	Simple Predicate

SKILLS

▶ **Exercise 3:** Identify each type of sentence by writing the correct label in the blank. (**Labels: S, F, SCS, SCV, CD**)

_____ 1. Sunlight shone through the stained-glass windows, and the colors were beautiful.
_____ 2. Several customers in the antique shop on the highway.
_____ 3. Jason, Sharon, and Evan had a picnic at Big Rock Mountain last weekend.
_____ 4. Monarch butterflies migrate in the autumn and may travel thousands of miles.

▶ **Exercise 4:** Use a slash to separate the two complete thoughts in each run-on sentence.
Correct the run-on sentences as indicated by the labels in parentheses at the end of each sentence.

1. The delivery company looked for our missing package the delivery company found it. (**CSV**)
_____

2. Mary Beth bought a new aquarium she needed some tropical fish. (**CD; therefore,**)
_____

EDITING

▶ **Exercise 5:** Correct each mistake. **Editing Guide: End Marks: 3   Capitals: 19   Commas: 3**
Subject / Verb Agreement: 1   Quotation Marks: 8   Misspelled Words: 2

henry wadsworth longfellow wove the history of america into many of his poems his poetrey are

based on clear and easily understood themes some of his poems include evangeline the song

of hiawatha the courtship of miles standish and the midnight ride of paul revere

Notes: _____

_____

_____

_____

_____

_____

_____

_____

_____

_____

_____

_____

_____

_____

_____

_____

_____

_____

_____

_____

_____

_____

_____

_____

_____

_____

_____

_____

_____

_____

_____

_____

_____

Classroom Practice 26

Name:_____ Date:_____

GRAMMAR

▶ **Exercise 1:** Classify each sentence.

1. _____ The blue city bus on our route did not come on time today.

2. _____ She often sang with Danny at the community building in Glenridge.

3. _____ Is the extra pizza in the kitchen covered with diced pineapple and ham?

SKILLS

▶ **Exercise 2:** Identify each type of sentence by writing the correct label in the blank. (**Labels: S, F, SCS, SCV, CD, CX**)

_____ 1. Our grandparents were happy when we rented an apartment near them.

_____ 2. After Sharon moved away, Laura spoke with her on the phone and by e-mail.

_____ 3. Squash and corn filled the bushel baskets at the roadside vegetable stand.

_____ 4. The obedient little girl did her chores and spoke politely to her parents.

_____ 5. Crystal icicles glittered in the bright sunlight, and new snow crunched under our feet.

_____ 6. The rickety old wooden bridge ahead.

▶ **Exercise 3:** Use a slash to separate the two complete thoughts in each run-on sentence.
Correct the run-on sentences as indicated by the labels in parentheses at the end of each sentence.

1. The fireworks burst overhead the little boy was astonished. (**CX when**) (1)

_____

2. The elderly woman was able to clean up her yard her neighbors helped her. (**CX because**) (2)

_____

3. Katherine always rode the elevator at the mall she used the stairs today. (**CD; however,**)

_____

EDITING

▶ **Exercise 4:** Correct each mistake. **Editing Guide: End Marks: 3   Capitals: 14   Commas: 5   Homonyms: 1**
A/An: 2   Subject / Verb Agreement: 1   Apostrophes: 1   Misspelled Words: 2

in 1876 albert spalding and james his brother started an sporting goods manufacturing company

in chicopee massachusetts during albert s pitching career with the boston red stockings he used an

bawl that he had designd this ball were the offical ball of the major leagues for more than 100 years

Notes: _____

Classroom Practice 27

Name:_____ Date:_____

GRAMMAR

▶ **Exercise 1:** Classify each sentence.

1. _____ Dangerous germs quickly spread in filthy environments.

2. _____ At night, the chickens and roosters do not roost in the large tree in their chicken pen.

SKILLS

▶ **Exercise 2:** Identify each type of sentence by writing the correct label in the blank. (**Labels: S, F, SCS, SCV, CD, CX**)

_____ 1. The tournament was rescheduled for next week.

_____ 2. The raccoons raided my corn patch; however, they didn't bother my tomatoes.

_____ 3. After she boarded the plane, Emma panicked.

_____ 4. Floodwaters and debris destroyed the cotton crop.

_____ 5. We saluted the flag as the school band played the national anthem.

▶ **Exercise 3:** Use a slash to separate the two complete thoughts in each run-on sentence. Correct the run-on sentences as indicated by the labels in parentheses at the end of each sentence.

1. We were in South America my older sister had her baby. (**CX while**) (1)

_____

2. My grandmother developed arthritis she had her sixtieth birthday. (**CX after**) (2)

_____

▶ **Exercise 4:** Identify each thought by putting a slash between each one. Then, use the Sentence Guide to combine related thoughts. Finally, underline simple sentences once, compound sentences twice, and put parentheses around complex sentences.
Sentence Guide: (Sentence 1–2: **CD**), (Sentences 3–5: **CX-since, CV**), (Sentences 6–7: **CX-because**), (Sentences 8–10: **SCV**), (Sentences 11–12: **CD**)

Dad was teaching my sister how to drive and they practiced every evening so I was curious about their progress and I went with them but I had to restrain my laughter the whole time and because she was learning on a stick shift my sister could not coordinate the clutch and the accelerator the car jerked and the car jumped and the car died at least 100 times but it was a fun experience and I'm glad I went.

_____

_____

_____

_____

_____

_____

_____

 **Homework 3**

Complete this homework assignment.

1. Copy the sentence below. Classify the sentence, using the Question and Answer Flow, as you label each part.

———— That beautiful leather sofa and matching chair were not discounted at the store .

2. Correct the run-on sentences on notebook paper by rewriting them as indicated by the labels in parentheses at the end of each sentence.

1. We waved farewell the train passed out of sight. (**CX as**) (2)

_____

2. Traffic on the freeway is heavy I take the access road. (**CX if**) (1)

_____

3. Aunt Martha is ninety years old she doesn't act it. (**CX even though**) (1)

_____

4. I had to go back to the store I forgot the bread. (**CX because**) (2)

_____

3. Write two complex sentences on notebook paper. For the first complex sentence, write the subordinate clause first and write the independent clause last. For the second complex sentence, write the independent clause first and write the subordinate clause last. Punctuate each complex sentence correctly.

Chapter 8 Checkup 28

Name:_____ Date:_____

GRAMMAR

▶ **Exercise 1:** Classify each sentence.

1. _____ During the thunderstorm, our tent suddenly collapsed and fell on our heads!

2. _____ The books on the shelves in the library were not arranged in alphabetical order.

SKILLS

▶ **Exercise 2:** Identify each type of sentence by writing the correct label in the blank. (**Labels: S, F, SCS, SCV, CD, CX**)

_____ 1. He complains about the elected officials, yet he never votes.

_____ 2. The newly-elected mayor of Brewster lives on Lincoln Boulevard.

_____ 3. Jacob and Jeremiah are on the school debate team.

_____ 4. She turned the oven on, but she forgot to set the temperature.

_____ 5. Since our chimney is filled with soot, we dare not build a fire in the fireplace.

▶ **Exercise 3:** Use a slash to separate the two complete thoughts in each run-on sentence. Correct the run-on sentences as indicated by the labels in parentheses at the end of each sentence.

1. We have our pictures taken I always have my eyes closed. (**CX whenever**) (**1**)

_____

2. I like green bell peppers jalapeños are too hot. (**CD but**) (**2**)

_____

3. I interviewed the football team I wrote the sports article. (**CX before**) (**2**)

_____

▶ **Exercise 4:** Use the Sentence Guide to combine related thoughts. Then, underline simple sentences once, compound sentences twice, and put parentheses around complex sentences.
Sentence Guide: (Sentences 1–2: **SCS**), (Sentences 3–4: **CD**), (Sentences 5–6: **SCV**), (Sentences 7–9: **CX-after, CV**)

[1]Ray wanted to catch the rabbit in their garden. [2]Beth wanted to catch the rabbit in their garden. [3]They looked for him everywhere. [4]They could not find him. [5]Finally, they gave up. [6]They went inside the house. [7]The door slammed. [8]The rabbit crawled from under an overturned flower pot. [9]It headed for the garden.

_____

_____

_____

_____

_____

Notes: _____

_____

_____

_____

_____

_____

_____

_____

_____

_____

_____

_____

_____

_____

_____

_____

_____

_____

_____

_____

_____

_____

_____

_____

_____

_____

_____

_____

_____

_____

Classroom Practice 29

Name: _____

Date: _____

INDEPENDENT PRACTICE & REVISED SENTENCES

1. Write a Practice Sentence according to the labels you choose.
   Use the **SN/SP V** as your main labels. You may use the other labels in any order and as many times as you wish in order to make a Practice Sentence.
   Chapter 8 labels for a Practice Sentence: SN/SP, V, Adj, Adv, A, P, OP, PPA, C, HV

2. Write a Revised Sentence. Use the following revision strategies: *synonym (syn), antonym (ant), word change (wc), added word (add), deleted word (delete), or no change (nc)*. Under each word, write the abbreviation of the revision strategy you use.

Labels:

Practice:

Revised:

Strategies:

Labels:

Practice:

Revised:

Strategies:

Labels:

Practice:

Revised:

Strategies:

Notes: _____

_____

_____

_____

_____

_____

_____

_____

_____

_____

_____

_____

_____

_____

_____

_____

_____

_____

_____

_____

_____

_____

_____

_____

_____

_____

_____

_____

Chapter 9 Writing Evaluation Guide

Name:_____ Date:_____

ROUGH DRAFT CHECK

_____ 1. Did you write your rough draft in pencil?

_____ 2. Did you write the correct headings on the first seven lines of your paper?

_____ 3. Did you use extra wide margins and skip every other line?

_____ 4. Did you write a title at the end of your rough draft?

_____ 5. Did you place your edited rough draft in your Rough Draft folder?

REVISING CHECK

_____ 6. Did you identify the purpose, type of writing, and audience?

_____ 7. Did you check for a topic, topic sentence, and sentences supporting the topic?

_____ 8. Did you check sentences for the right order, and did you combine, rearrange, or delete sentences when necessary?

_____ 9. Did you check for a variety of simple, compound, and complex sentences?

_____ 10. Did you check for any left out, repeated, or unnecessary words?

_____ 11. Did you check for the best choice of words by replacing or deleting unclear words?

_____ 12. Did you check the content for interest and creativity?

_____ 13. Did you check the voice to make sure the writing says what you want it to say?

EDITING CHECK

_____ 14. Did you indent each paragraph?

_____ 15. Did you put an end mark at the end of every sentence?

_____ 16. Did you capitalize the first word of every sentence?

_____ 17. Did you check for all other capitalization mistakes?

_____ 18. Did you check for all punctuation mistakes?
(commas, periods, apostrophes, quotation marks, underlining)

_____ 19. Did you check for misspelled words and for incorrect homonym choices?

_____ 20. Did you check for incorrect spellings of plural and possessive forms?

_____ 21. Did you check for correct construction and punctuation of your sentences?

_____ 22. Did you check for usage mistakes? _(subject/verb agreement, a/an choices, contractions, verb tenses, pronoun/antecedent agreement, pronoun cases, degrees of adjectives, double negatives, etc.)_

_____ 23. Did you put your revised and edited paper in the Rough Draft folder?

FINAL PAPER CHECK

_____ 24. Did you write the final paper in pencil?

_____ 25. Did you center the title on the top line and center your name under the title?

_____ 26. Did you skip a line before starting the writing assignment?

_____ 27. Did you single-space, use wide margins, and write the final paper neatly?

_____ 28. Did you staple your papers in this order: final paper on top, rough draft in the middle, and prewriting map on the bottom? Did you put them in the Final Paper folder?

Notes: _____

_____

_____

_____

_____

_____

_____

_____

_____

_____

_____

_____

_____

_____

_____

_____

_____

_____

_____

_____

_____

_____

_____

_____

_____

_____

_____

_____

_____

_____

_____

_____

_____

Chapter 9 Checkup 30

Name:_____ Date:_____

SKILLS

Read the article below and make an outline. Use References 73–77 to review outlining.

ARTICLE:	OUTLINE:

Bats

What mammal has wings AND hands? A bat! There are approximately a thousand different species of bats, and they are among some of the most fascinating mammals to study.

Bats live in a variety of locations throughout the world. A few species can live in extremely cold places like Alaska and Finland. However, most bats prefer moderate to warm climates, especially the climates in rainforests and tropical areas.

Bats live in many types of homes. Bats usually make their homes in dark places where they can be protected from weather or predators. Probably the most common place for bats to roost is in caves. Some bats also live in trees. Bats find several places in the trees to roost, such as in holes of trees, under large leaves, or under the bark of some trees. Buildings and houses sometimes provide a comfortable, safe roosting area, as do bridges and underground tunnels.

Bats eat many different kinds of food. Almost all species of bats eat insects, especially mosquitoes. Some bats crave ripe, sweet fruit, while others eat birds. The famed Vampire bat dines on the blood of other animals! Other bats eat fish. Amazingly, these bats locate fish by echolocation, a type of sonar. Then, they pluck the fish from the water.

Bats are truly remarkable creatures worthy of our respect. Besides their unique characteristics, they are useful for controlling the insect population throughout the world.

Notes: _____

Classroom Practice 32

Name:_____ Date:_____

GRAMMAR

▶ **Exercise 1:** Classify each sentence.

1. _____ Oh my! A large flock of geese suddenly swooped into my grandpa's cornfields!

2. _____ Sweep and mop carefully under the table in the kitchen.

▶ **Exercise 2:** Name the eight parts of speech that you have studied so far.

1._____   3._____   5._____   7._____

2._____   4._____   6._____   8._____

SKILLS

▶ **Exercise 3: For Part A**, underline each noun to be made possessive. Write **S** for singular or **P** for plural, the rule number, and the possessive form. **For Part B**, write the singular possessive and plural possessive of each noun.

RULE 1: **boy's** For a singular noun — add ('s)	RULE 2: **boys'** For a plural noun that ends in s — add (')	RULE 3: **men's** For a plural noun that does not end in s — add ('s)

Part A	S-P	Rule	Possessive Form	Part B	Singular Poss	Plural Poss
1. geese feathers				6. radio		
2. quartets songs				7. wife		
3. Morris desk				8. leaf		
4. octopus beak				9. pilot		
5. pianist solo				10. airport		

▶ **Exercise 4:** Identify each type of sentence by writing the correct label in the blank. (**Labels: S, F, SCS, SCV, CD, CX, CD-CX**)

_____ 1. Faithful friends brought Diane food and treats until she recuperated.
_____ 2. The electricity went off; consequently, we slept by the fireplace until we had heat again.
_____ 3. Extreme thirst and aching muscles kept Julia up all night.
_____ 4. Someone knows the combination to my lock and has opened my locker!
_____ 5. Ethan played on the gym set, and Addison dug in the sandbox.
_____ 6. Noisy cicadas buzzed annoyingly one hot summer night.

▶ **Exercise 5:** Use a slash to separate the complete thoughts in each run-on sentence. Correct the run-on sentences as indicated by the labels in parentheses at the end of each sentence.

1. You go to the store I need shampoo Leah needs toothpaste. **CD-CX: (1) Sub-whenever (2) CD, and**

_____

2. We stood in line for popcorn they sold out the movie began. **CD-CX: (1) CD, but (2) Sub-before**

_____

Notes: _____

_____

_____

_____

_____

_____

_____

_____

_____

_____

_____

_____

_____

_____

_____

_____

_____

_____

_____

_____

_____

_____

_____

_____

_____

_____

_____

_____

_____

_____

_____

_____

Classroom Practice 33

Name:_____ Date:_____

GRAMMAR

▶ **Exercise 1:** Classify each sentence.

1. _____ Practice on your drums in your friend's basement.

2. _____ Will the hole in the side of my cousin's garage be repaired before winter?

SKILLS

▶ **Exercise 2:** Place a **CE** in the blanks before those sentence pairs which are arranged in a cause-effect relationship. Place an **EC** in those blanks before the sentence pairs which are arranged in an effect-cause relationship.

_____ 1. Because the ground was unusually cold, the seeds would not sprout.
_____ 2. Dad will be late for dinner because his plane was delayed in Memphis.
_____ 3. Since Todd has begun exercising, he has lost thirty-five pounds.
_____ 4. She is allergic to aspirin; therefore, she uses a different pain reliever.

▶ **Exercise 3: For Part A**, underline each noun to be made possessive. Write **S** for singular or **P** for plural, the rule number, and the possessive form. **For Part B**, write the singular possessive and plural possessive of each noun.

RULE 1: boy's	RULE 2: boys'	RULE 3: men's
For a singular noun — add ('s)	For a plural noun that ends in s — add (')	For a plural noun that does not end in s — add ('s)

Part A	S-P	Rule	Possessive Form	Part B	Singular Poss	Plural Poss
1. ocean waves				6. dancer		
2. coffee aroma				7. man		
3. electricians wire				8. pelican		
4. children music				9. patio		
5. Stacey purse				10. branch		

▶ **Exercise 4:** Identify each type of sentence by writing the correct label in the blank. (**Labels: S, F, SCS, SCV, CD, CX, CD-CX**)

_____ 1. After Cliff changed his flat tire in the rain, he continued wearily on his journey.
_____ 2. I bought a new suit, and my wife bought a new dress before we left for Hawaii.
_____ 3. A basket of cheerful daisies sat on the kitchen counter.
_____ 4. My mother has a cast on her leg and cannot drive for six weeks.
_____ 5. Lightning struck the ancient tree, and it fell to the ground.

▶ **Exercise 5:** Use a slash to separate the complete thoughts in each run-on sentence.
Correct the run-on sentences as indicated by the labels in parentheses at the end of each sentence.

1. Jill's father is a publisher he is also an artist he has spare time. **CD-CX: (1) CD-and (2) Sub-when**

_____

2. I drank a bottle of water I was still thirsty my mouth was dry. **CD-CX: (1) Sub-although (2) CD-and**

_____

 **Homework 4**

Complete this homework assignment.

1. Copy the sentence below. Classify the sentence, using the Question and Answer Flow, as you label each part.

_____ Are most cave formations in this area made of limestone?

2. Correct the run-on sentences on notebook paper by rewriting them as indicated by the labels in parentheses at the end of each sentence.

1. I called twice no one answered. **(CD; however,)**

_____

2. Dad will be furious I lose his camera. **(CX if) (2)**

_____

3. Our large tree blew over I called my dad he came right home. **CD-CX: (1) Sub-when (2) CD-and**

_____

3. Place a **CE** in the blanks before those sentence pairs which are arranged in a cause-effect relationship. Place an **EC** in those blanks before the sentence pairs which are arranged in an effect-cause relationship.

_____ 1. Since Meredith is my sister, we can go backstage after the play.

_____ 2. I will not tell anyone about your mistake since you are embarrassed.

_____ 3. Our yard always looks very nice because Dad and Colin mow every Saturday.

_____ 4. The magician was talented; therefore, we enjoyed the show.

4. Write a compound sentence, a complex sentence, and a compound-complex sentence on notebook paper. Punctuate each type of sentence correctly. Underline the conjunctions in all your sentences. Discuss your sentences with parents, a study partner, or in small groups.

Chapter 10 Checkup 34

Name:_____ Date:_____

GRAMMAR

▶ **Exercise 1:** Classify each sentence.

1. _____ Her lungs could not adjust to the high altitude of the mountain.

2. _____ Oh no! My brother's puppy is chewing on my math homework for today!

SKILLS

▶ **Exercise 2:** Place a **CE** in the blanks before those sentence pairs which are arranged in a cause-effect relationship. Place an **EC** in those blanks before the sentence pairs which are arranged in an effect-cause relationship.

_____ 1. Since I did not have to get up early, I stayed late at the neighbor's block party.

_____ 2. The council members became quite upset because the mayor vetoed their proposal.

_____ 3. We had no rain in August; therefore, our flower beds are ruined.

_____ 4. Last summer, I attended a class on gardening since I like to learn new things.

▶ **Exercise 3: For Part A**, underline each noun to be made possessive. Write **S** for singular or **P** for plural, the rule number, and the possessive form. **For Part B**, write the singular possessive and plural possessive of each noun.

RULE 1: **boy's**	RULE 2: **boys'**	RULE 3: **men's**
For a singular noun — add ('s)	For a plural noun that ends in s — add (')	For a plural noun that does not end in s — add ('s)

Part A	S-P	Rule	Possessive Form	Part B	Singular Poss	Plural Poss
1. mice paws				6. giraffe		
2. bride gown				7. parrot		
3. owner manual				8. carpet		
4. bikers trails				9. pass		
5. Carlos mustache				10. woman		

▶ **Exercise 4:** Identify each type of sentence by writing the correct label in the blank. (**Labels: S, F, SCS, SCV, CD, CX, CD-CX**)

_____ 1. Most wild animals will not attack unless they are cornered.

_____ 2. The chef prepared the grilled salmon and placed it on the buffet.

_____ 3. Before she plunged into the pool, she posed for a picture, and we applauded.

_____ 4. Armadillos and opossums wander near Southern highways on summer nights.

_____ 5. Shelby lost her car keys on Thursday, and she did not sleep a wink that night.

▶ **Exercise 5:** Use a slash to separate the complete thoughts in each run-on sentence. Correct the run-on sentences as indicated by the labels in parentheses at the end of each sentence.

1. We left on vacation my sister kept our cat my aunt fed our dogs. **CD-CX: (1) sub-when (2) CD-and**

_____

2. I love homemade peach ice cream I eat it I can. **CD-CX: (1) CD-and (2) sub-whenever**

_____

Notes: _____

_____

_____

_____

_____

_____

_____

_____

_____

_____

_____

_____

_____

_____

_____

_____

_____

_____

_____

_____

_____

_____

_____

_____

_____

_____

_____

_____

Classroom Practice 35

Name: _____   Date: _____

INDEPENDENT PRACTICE & REVISED SENTENCES

1. Write a Practice Sentence according to the labels you choose.
   Use the **SN/SP V** as your main labels. You may use the other labels in any order and as many times as you wish in order to make a Practice Sentence.
   Chapter 10 labels for a Practice Sentence: SN/SP, V, Adj, Adv, A, P, OP, PPA, C, HV, I, PNA

2. Write a Revised Sentence. Use the following revision strategies: *synonym (syn), antonym (ant), word change (wc), added word (add), deleted word (delete),* or *no change (nc).* Under each word, write the abbreviation of the revision strategy you use.

Labels:

Practice:

Revised:

Strategies:

Labels:

Practice:

Revised:

Strategies:

Labels:

Practice:

Revised:

Strategies:

SHURLEY ENGLISH

Notes: _____

_____

_____

_____

_____

_____

_____

_____

_____

_____

_____

_____

_____

_____

_____

_____

_____

_____

_____

_____

_____

_____

_____

_____

_____

_____

_____

_____

Chapter 11 Writing Evaluation Guide

Name:_____ Date:_____

ROUGH DRAFT CHECK

_____ 1. Did you write your rough draft in pencil?

_____ 2. Did you write the correct headings on the first seven lines of your paper?

_____ 3. Did you use extra wide margins and skip every other line?

_____ 4. Did you write a title at the end of your rough draft?

_____ 5. Did you place your edited rough draft in your Rough Draft folder?

REVISING CHECK

_____ 6. Did you identify the purpose, type of writing, and audience?

_____ 7. Did you check for a topic, topic sentence, and sentences supporting the topic?

_____ 8. Did you check sentences for the right order, and did you combine, rearrange, or delete sentences when necessary?

_____ 9. Did you check for a variety of simple, compound, and complex sentences?

_____ 10. Did you check for any left out, repeated, or unnecessary words?

_____ 11. Did you check for the best choice of words by replacing or deleting unclear words?

_____ 12. Did you check the content for interest and creativity?

_____ 13. Did you check the voice to make sure the writing says what you want it to say?

EDITING CHECK

_____ 14. Did you indent each paragraph?

_____ 15. Did you put an end mark at the end of every sentence?

_____ 16. Did you capitalize the first word of every sentence?

_____ 17. Did you check for all other capitalization mistakes?

_____ 18. Did you check for all punctuation mistakes?
(commas, periods, apostrophes, quotation marks, underlining)

_____ 19. Did you check for misspelled words and for incorrect homonym choices?

_____ 20. Did you check for incorrect spellings of plural and possessive forms?

_____ 21. Did you check for correct construction and punctuation of your sentences?

_____ 22. Did you check for usage mistakes? (subject/verb agreement, a/an choices, contractions, verb tenses, pronoun/antecedent agreement, pronoun cases, degrees of adjectives, double negatives, etc.)

_____ 23. Did you put your revised and edited paper in the Rough Draft folder?

FINAL PAPER CHECK

_____ 24. Did you write the final paper in pencil?

_____ 25. Did you center the title on the top line and center your name under the title?

_____ 26. Did you skip a line before starting the writing assignment?

_____ 27. Did you single-space, use wide margins, and write the final paper neatly?

_____ 28. Did you staple your papers in this order: final paper on top, rough draft in the middle, and prewriting map on the bottom? Did you put them in the Final Paper folder?

Notes: _____

_____

_____

_____

_____

_____

_____

_____

_____

_____

_____

_____

_____

_____

_____

_____

_____

_____

_____

_____

_____

_____

_____

_____

_____

_____

_____

_____

_____

_____

_____

_____

_____

_____

Classroom Practice 36

Name:_____ Date:_____

GRAMMAR

▶ **Exercise 1:** Classify each sentence.

1. _____ Yesterday, we picked a bushel of ripe peaches from the orchard.

2. _____ My friend and I heard many strange sounds outside our tent in the woods.

▶ **Exercise 2:** Use Sentence 2 above to complete the table below.

List the Noun Used	List the Noun Job	Singular or Plural	Common or Proper	Simple Subject	Simple Predicate

▶ **Exercise 3:** Choose the part of speech for the underlined word.

1. Beavers <u>and</u> otters enjoy water. ☐verb ☐noun ☐adjective ☐adverb ☐conjunction ☐pronoun

2. Bonnie answered the <u>phone</u> during my break. ☐verb ☐noun ☐adjective ☐adverb ☐conjunction ☐pronoun

SKILLS

▶ **Exercise 4:** Place a **CE** in the blanks before those sentence pairs which are arranged in a cause-effect relationship. Place an **EC** in those blanks before the sentence pairs which are arranged in an effect-cause relationship.

_____ 1. I took a course on childcare because I plan to baby-sit this summer.

_____ 2. Bo and Jan had planned for an emergency; therefore, they did not run out of money.

_____ 3. Since Jonathan graduated, he has been working at the library full-time.

_____ 4. Because Terrell's meeting lasted three hours, he was late for his dentist appointment.

▶ **Exercise 5:** Identify each type of sentence by writing the correct label in the blank. (**Labels: S, F, SCS, SCV, CD, CX, CD-CX**)

_____ 1. Slugs, snails, and moles have destroyed Elizabeth's vegetable garden.

_____ 2. After the store closes, we will need to restock the shelves.

_____ 3. The squirrel scampered up the tree and dined on several hickory nuts.

_____ 4. We waited in line for over an hour; however, David had already purchased his ticket.

_____ 5. When I was little, I loved cartoons, and I still find a few of them amusing.

▶ **Exercise 6:** Use a slash to separate the complete thoughts in each run-on sentence.
Correct the run-on sentences as indicated by the labels in parentheses at the end of each sentence.

1. We leave the mall we will go to the coffee shop Julie will meet us there. **CD-CX (1) Sub-after (2) CD-and**

_____

2. Kathy plays the guitar Keri sings they get together. **CD-CX (1) CD-and (2) Sub-whenever**

_____

SHURLEY ENGLISH

Notes: _____

_____

_____

_____

_____

_____

_____

_____

_____

_____

_____

_____

_____

_____

_____

_____

_____

_____

_____

_____

_____

_____

_____

_____

_____

_____

_____

_____

_____

_____

_____

_____

_____

Classroom Practice 37

Name:_____ Date:_____

GRAMMAR

▶ **Exercise 1:** Classify each sentence.

1. _____ Set an extra plate on the table for an unexpected guest for dinner tonight.

2. _____ My mother and sister made sandwiches, a salad, and a coconut cake for the party.

3. _____ Fast-sailing ships from New York carried supplies to California during the Gold Rush.

▶ **Exercise 2:** Use Sentence 3 above to complete the table below.

List the Noun Used	List the Noun Job	Singular or Plural	Common or Proper	Simple Subject	Simple Predicate

SKILLS

▶ **Exercise 3:** List the present-tense and past-tense helping verbs in the blanks below.

Present Tense	1.	2.	3.	4.	5.	6.	7.
Past Tense	1.	2.	3.	4.	5.		

▶ **Exercise 4:** Write **R** for regular or **I** for irregular. Then, write the past-tense form.

1. buy ____ **Past tense:** _____   3. move ____ **Past tense:** _____   5. do ____ **Past tense:** _____

2. color ____ **Past tense:** _____   4. speak ____ **Past tense:** _____   6. point ____ **Past tense:** _____

▶ **Exercise 5:** (1) Underline the verb or verb phrase. (2) Identify the verb tense by writing **1** for present or present-perfect tense, **2** for past or past-perfect tense, or **3** for future or future-perfect tense. (3) Write the past-tense form. (4) Write **R** for Regular or **I** for Irregular.

	Verb Tense	Main Verb Past Tense Form	R or I
1. Exotic spiders were displayed behind glass.			
2. The engineer is drawing plans for the bridge.			
3. The judges will announce winners soon.			
4. Melvin and Jo are purchasing a new vehicle.			
5. His goats had eaten all of the hay.			
6. Mr. West will survey your property at noon.			

Notes: _____

_____

_____

_____

_____

_____

_____

_____

_____

_____

_____

_____

_____

_____

_____

_____

_____

_____

_____

_____

_____

_____

_____

_____

_____

_____

_____

_____

_____

_____

Classroom Practice 38, Part A

Name:_____ Date:_____

GRAMMAR

▶ **Exercise 1:** Classify each sentence.

1. _____ Water the houseplants on the veranda.

2. _____ Two students in our class did not complete their English homework.

3. _____ Did the severe thunderstorm move into your area about midnight?

▶ **Exercise 2:** Use Sentence 2 above to complete the table below.

List the Noun Used	List the Noun Job	Singular or Plural	Common or Proper	Simple Subject	Simple Predicate

▶ **Exercise 3:** Write only the pattern number in the blank. Use these patterns: **P1-SN V**   **P2-SN V-t DO**

_____ 1. We did not buy a new truck today.

_____ 2. Patrick cut his leg on the rusty bolt.

_____ 3. Look for your hat in the loft of the barn.

_____ 4. The tired workers went home at midnight.

_____ 5. The bus crossed the busy intersection safely.

_____ 6. Was the airplane flying low over the mountains?

_____ 7. The almonds and chestnuts were roasting over an open fire.

_____ 8. The summer drought left many small communities without water.

_____ 9. Did William and Meg leave for their vacation early in the morning?

_____ 10. The two custodians buffed the scarred floor during the nighttime hours.

EDITING

▶ **Exercise 4:** Correct each mistake. **Editing Guide: End Marks: 4   Capitals: 5   Commas: 1   Homonyms: 3   Subject / Verb Agreement: 4   Misspelled Words: 2**

my brother and my dad is louzy shoppers mom give them a list and they returns with wrong

items they buys the wrong serial and coal slaw instead of macarroni salad pour mom

Classroom Practice 38, Part B

Name:_____ Date:_____

SKILLS

▶ **Exercise 5:** Write the four principal parts of the following verbs: **depart** and **choose**.

_____ _____ _____ _____

_____ _____ _____ _____

▶ **Exercise 6:** Conjugate the verbs listed below.

Verb Conjugation	Present	Past	Future	Present Perfect	Past Perfect	Future Perfect
For the regular verb: **talk**						
For the irregular verb: **fall**						

▶ **Exercise 7:** List the present-tense and past-tense helping verbs in the blanks below.

Present Tense	1.	2.	3.	4.	5.	6.	7.
Past Tense	1.	2.	3.	4.	5.		

▶ **Exercise 8:** Write **R** for regular or **I** for irregular. Then, write the past-tense form.

1. search ____ **Past tense:** _____   3. say ____ **Past tense:** _____   5. wear ____ **Past tense:** _____

2. freeze ____ **Past tense:** _____   4. paint ____ **Past tense:** _____   6. discuss ____ **Past tense:** _____

▶ **Exercise 9:** (1) Underline the verb or verb phrase. (2) Identify the verb tense by writing **1** for present or present-perfect tense, **2** for past or past-perfect tense, or **3** for future or future-perfect tense. (3) Write the past-tense form. (4) Write **R** for Regular or **I** for Irregular.

	Verb Tense	Main Verb Past Tense Form	R or I
1. Tiny violets bloom along the mossy riverbank.			
2. A gray-haired man bought tickets to our play.			
3. Fifty ballerinas will appear on the stage.			
4. He wrote an original poem for the event.			
5. Nicole and Lori attend a school in Oregon.			
6. Meteorologists will report any severe weather.			
7. The elderly ladies giggled like little girls.			
8. Jane teaches a literature class in the fall.			
9. We watched superhero movies all weekend.			
10. I will purchase a case of maple syrup.			

Homework 5

Complete this homework assignment.

1. Write **Present Tense** beside Number 1 and list the present-tense helping verbs. Write **Past Tense** beside Number 2 and list the past-tense helping verbs. Write **Future Tense** beside Number 3 and list the future-tense helping verbs.

Present Tense: _____, _____, _____, _____, _____, _____, _____

Past Tense: _____, _____, _____, _____, _____

Future tense: _____, _____

2. For each sentence, do four things. (1) Underline the verb or verb phrase. (2) Identify the verb tense by writing **1** for present or present-perfect tense, **2** for past or past-perfect tense, or **3** for future or future-perfect tense. (3) Write the past-tense form. (4) Write **R** for Regular or **I** for Irregular.

	Verb Tense	Main Verb Past Tense Form	R or I
1. Our mom sells real estate as a hobby.			
2. We will parachute out of the plane at 3,000 feet.			
3. The supervisor wrote a voucher for free merchandise.			
4. Tonya brought brownies and ice cream to the party.			
5. Our meeting with the lawyer usually lasts until 4:00.			
6. Uncle Matthew polished his antique car for the show.			
7. The prices will rise before the holidays.			

3. Write the four principal parts of the following verbs: **plan** and **give**.

_____   _____   _____

_____   _____   _____   _____

4. Conjugate the verbs listed below.

Verb Conjugation	Present	Past	Future	Present Perfect	Past Perfect	Future Perfect
For the regular verb: **carry**						
For the irregular verb: **choose**						

Notes: _____

_____

_____

_____

_____

_____

_____

_____

_____

_____

_____

_____

_____

_____

_____

_____

_____

_____

_____

_____

_____

_____

_____

_____

_____

_____

_____

_____

_____

Chapter 12 Checkup 39

Name:_____ Date:_____

GRAMMAR

▶ **Exercise 1:** Classify each sentence.

1. _____ As treasurer, I wrote several checks for the company over the weekend.

2. _____ Yikes! That fearsome crocodile turned and lunged quickly forward toward the worker!

SKILLS

▶ **Exercise 2:** Write the four principal parts of the following verbs: **climb** and **lose**.

_____   _____   _____   _____

_____   _____   _____   _____

▶ **Exercise 3:** Conjugate the verbs listed below.

Verb Conjugation	Present	Past	Future	Present Perfect	Past Perfect	Future Perfect
For the regular verb: **hurry**						
For the irregular verb: **become**						

▶ **Exercise 4:** (1) Underline the verb or verb phrase. (2) Identify the verb tense by writing **1** for present or present-perfect tense, **2** for past or past-perfect tense, or **3** for future or future-perfect tense. (3) Write the past-tense form. (4) Write **R** for Regular or **I** for Irregular.

	Verb Tense	Main Verb Past Tense Form	R or I
1. Our family will travel to Colorado at night.			
2. The runners become dehydrated very quickly.			
3. The afternoon sun left a pink streak in the sky.			
4. The porpoises will vault onto the platform.			

▶ **Exercise 5:** Write **R** for regular or **I** for irregular. Then, write the past-tense form.

1. sleep ____ Past tense: _____   3. turn ____ Past tense: _____   5. hunt ____ Past tense: _____

2. destroy ____ Past tense: _____   4. see ____ Past tense: _____   6. know ____ Past tense: _____

▶ **Exercise 6:** List the present-tense and past-tense helping verbs in the blanks below.

Present Tense	1.	2.	3.	4.	5.	6.	7.
Past Tense	1.	2.	3.	4.	5.		

Notes: _____

_____

_____

_____

_____

_____

_____

_____

_____

_____

_____

_____

_____

_____

_____

_____

_____

_____

_____

_____

_____

_____

_____

_____

_____

_____

_____

_____

_____

_____

_____

_____

Classroom Practice 40

Name: _____   Date: _____

INDEPENDENT PRACTICE & REVISED SENTENCES

1. Write a Practice Sentence according to the labels you choose.
Use the SN/SP, V-t, DO as your main labels. You may use the other labels in any order and as many times as you wish in order to make a Practice Sentence.
Chapter 12 labels for a Practice Sentence: SN/SP, V-t, DO, Adj, Adv, A, P, OP, PPA, C, HV, I, PNA

2. Write a Revised Sentence. Use the following revision strategies: *synonym (syn), antonym (ant), word change (wc), added word (add), deleted word (delete),* or *no change (nc).* Under each word, write the abbreviation of the revision strategy you use.

Labels: _____

Practice: _____

Revised: _____

Strategies: _____

Labels: _____

Practice: _____

Revised: _____

Strategies: _____

Labels: _____

Practice: _____

Revised: _____

Strategies: _____

Notes: _____

_____

_____

_____

_____

_____

_____

_____

_____

_____

_____

_____

_____

_____

_____

_____

_____

_____

_____

_____

_____

_____

_____

_____

_____

_____

_____

_____

_____

_____

_____

Chapter 13 Writing Evaluation Guide

Name:_____ Date:_____

ROUGH DRAFT CHECK

_____ 1. Did you write your rough draft in pencil?

_____ 2. Did you write the correct headings on the first seven lines of your paper?

_____ 3. Did you use extra wide margins and skip every other line?

_____ 4. Did you write a title at the end of your rough draft?

_____ 5. Did you place your edited rough draft in your Rough Draft folder?

REVISING CHECK

_____ 6. Did you identify the purpose, type of writing, and audience?

_____ 7. Did you check for a topic, topic sentence, and sentences supporting the topic?

_____ 8. Did you check sentences for the right order, and did you combine, rearrange, or delete sentences when necessary?

_____ 9. Did you check for a variety of simple, compound, and complex sentences?

_____ 10. Did you check for any left out, repeated, or unnecessary words?

_____ 11. Did you check for the best choice of words by replacing or deleting unclear words?

_____ 12. Did you check the content for interest and creativity?

_____ 13. Did you check the voice to make sure the writing says what you want it to say?

EDITING CHECK

_____ 14. Did you indent each paragraph?

_____ 15. Did you put an end mark at the end of every sentence?

_____ 16. Did you capitalize the first word of every sentence?

_____ 17. Did you check for all other capitalization mistakes?

_____ 18. Did you check for all punctuation mistakes? *(commas, periods, apostrophes, quotation marks, underlining)*

_____ 19. Did you check for misspelled words and for incorrect homonym choices?

_____ 20. Did you check for incorrect spellings of plural and possessive forms?

_____ 21. Did you check for correct construction and punctuation of your sentences?

_____ 22. Did you check for usage mistakes? *(subject/verb agreement, a/an choices, contractions, verb tenses, pronoun/antecedent agreement, pronoun cases, degrees of adjectives, double negatives, etc.)*

_____ 23. Did you put your revised and edited paper in the Rough Draft folder?

FINAL PAPER CHECK

_____ 24. Did you write the final paper in pencil?

_____ 25. Did you center the title on the top line and center your name under the title?

_____ 26. Did you skip a line before starting the writing assignment?

_____ 27. Did you single-space, use wide margins, and write the final paper neatly?

_____ 28. Did you staple your papers in this order: final paper on top, rough draft in the middle, and prewriting map on the bottom? Did you put them in the Final Paper folder?

Notes: _____

_____

_____

_____

_____

_____

_____

_____

_____

_____

_____

_____

_____

_____

_____

_____

_____

_____

_____

_____

_____

_____

_____

_____

_____

_____

_____

_____

_____

Classroom Practice 41

Name:_____ Date:_____

GRAMMAR

▶ **Exercise 1:** Classify each sentence.

1. _____ The famous writer showed me the first draft of his new book.

2. _____ The elegant restaurant gave me a new uniform for my job as a waitress.

3. _____ Tonight, the entertaining comedian gave my friends and me some great laughs.

▶ **Exercise 2:** Use Sentence 3 above to complete the table below.

List the Noun Used	List the Noun Job	Singular or Plural	Common or Proper	Simple Subject	Simple Predicate

SKILLS

▶ **Exercise 3:** Change the underlined mixed-tense verbs in Paragraph 1 to present-tense verbs in Paragraph 2.

Paragraph 1: Mixed Tenses

Suddenly, Mrs. Montclair's computer <u>crashed</u>. She <u>does</u> nothing bad to it. One moment it <u>was</u> fine, and the next moment it just <u>goes</u> blank. Mr. Ferris, the technical support person for our school, <u>comes</u> to our classroom. After he <u>works</u> for a while, he <u>gets</u> it back up. Too bad Mrs. Montclair <u>did</u> not regularly <u>save</u> her work. She <u>loses</u> many documents. She <u>says</u> even some of our grades <u>were</u> missing. I <u>tell</u> her that maybe only the bad grades <u>were</u> missing, but she <u>does</u> not <u>think</u> that <u>is</u> very funny.

Paragraph 2: Present Tense

Suddenly, Mrs. Montclair's computer _____. She _____ nothing bad to it. One moment it _____ fine, and the next moment it just _____ blank. Mr. Ferris, the technical support person for our school, _____ to our classroom. After he _____ for a while, he _____ it back up. Too bad Mrs. Montclair _____ not regularly _____ her work. She _____ many documents. She _____ that even some of our grades _____ missing. I _____ her that maybe only the bad grades _____ missing, but she _____ not _____ that _____ very funny.

▶ **Exercise 4:** Conjugate the verb listed below.

Verb Conjugation	Present	Past	Future	Present Perfect	Past Perfect	Future Perfect
For the irregular verb: **catch**						

Notes: _____

_____

_____

_____

_____

_____

_____

_____

_____

_____

_____

_____

_____

_____

_____

_____

_____

_____

_____

_____

_____

_____

_____

_____

_____

_____

_____

_____

_____

_____

Classroom Practice 42

Name:_____ Date:_____

GRAMMAR

▶ **Exercise 1:** Classify each sentence.

1. _____ Did your English teacher give you a special assignment for second semester?

2. _____ Over the weekend, Sam and Joe baked me a surprise birthday cake for my party.

▶ **Exercise 2:** Use Sentence 2 above to complete the table below.

List the Noun Used	List the Noun Job	Singular or Plural	Common or Proper	Simple Subject	Simple Predicate

SKILLS

▶ **Exercise 3:** Underline the verb or verb phrase in each of these sentences. Then, indicate the voice of the verbs in each sentence by putting an **A**(active) or **P**(passive) in the blank before each sentence.

_____ 1. The gorilla had been fed bananas and vegetables.

_____ 2. Dad plants cabbage along the fence line.

_____ 3. The mouse was trapped in the closet.

_____ 4. Violets bloom along the pathway to the lake.

▶ **Exercise 4:** Change the underlined mixed-tense verbs in Paragraph 1 to present-tense verbs in Paragraph 2.

Paragraph 1: Mixed Tenses

We <u>need</u> a playground on the vacant lot by the bank. First, we <u>got</u> permission from the city. Then, we <u>began</u>. Student volunteers <u>clear</u> the lot. They also <u>cleaned</u> out an old shed. Church groups <u>rake</u> up the weeds, while bank employees <u>shoveled</u> garbage into bags. Our fire department <u>hauled</u> the stuff to the dump. We <u>decide</u> that the playground <u>needed</u> a walkway. A concrete company <u>provides</u> the cement, which construction workers <u>use</u> for the sidewalk. Our gardening club <u>bought</u> trees, which they <u>plant</u> along the walkway. Finally, a local store <u>donated</u> swings and slides. Our playground <u>is</u> ready for kids!

Paragraph 2: Present Tense

We _____ a playground on the vacant lot by the bank. First, we _____ permission from the city. Then, we _____. Student volunteers _____ the lot. They also _____ out an old shed. Church groups _____ up the weeds, while bank employees _____ garbage into bags. Our fire department _____ the stuff to the dump. We _____ that the playground _____ a walkway. A concrete company _____ the cement, which construction workers _____ for the sidewalk. Our gardening club _____ trees, which they _____ along the walkway. Finally, a local store _____ swings and slides. Our playground _____ ready for kids!

Notes: _____

_____

_____

_____

_____

_____

_____

_____

_____

_____

_____

_____

_____

_____

_____

_____

_____

_____

_____

_____

_____

_____

_____

_____

_____

_____

_____

_____

_____

Classroom Practice 43, Part A

Name:_____ Date:_____

GRAMMAR

▶ **Exercise 1:** Classify each sentence.

1. _____ The fresh bear tracks in the mud along the trail alarmed the hikers.

2. _____ Wow! Yesterday, Sally's brother bought her a motorcycle for her birthday!

3. _____ Tardy slips were given to students in the hallway after the second bell.

▶ **Exercise 2:** Use Sentence 1 above to complete the table below.

List the Noun Used	List the Noun Job	Singular or Plural	Common or Proper	Simple Subject	Simple Predicate

▶ **Exercise 3:** Write only the pattern number in the blank. Use these patterns:
   P1 SN V   P2 SN V-t DO   P3 SN V-t IO DO

_____ 1. Pass me the roast beef and mashed potatoes.

_____ 2. Did James and John look for the others at their sister's wedding reception?

_____ 3. The basketball fans rode the school bus to the state basketball finals.

_____ 4. I wanted peach cobbler with ice cream for dessert.

_____ 5. Teach Johnny and me a few basic rules about fishing for bass.

_____ 6. Our new neighbors generously offered us their cottage on the lake for two weeks!

_____ 7. In the desert, the temperature dips drastically at night.

_____ 8. The process of erosion changes the shape of the landforms.

_____ 9. Can you make me a good deal on that new Mustang GT?

_____ 10. An angry alligator attacked a ranger on patrol near the swamp.

SHURLEY ENGLISH

Classroom Practice 43, Part B

Name:_____ Date:_____

SKILLS

▶ **Exercise 4:** Underline the verb or verb phrase in each of these sentences. Then, indicate the voice of the verbs in each sentence by putting an **A** (active) or **P** (passive) in the blank before each sentence.

_____ 1. The farmer's chicken was killed by a speeding motorist.

_____ 2. My aunt celebrated her ninetieth birthday on Friday.

_____ 3. Termites destroyed the foundation of the old log house.

_____ 4. A steel vault was stolen from the local pawn shop.

▶ **Exercise 5:** Change the underlined mixed-tense verbs in Paragraph 1 to present-tense verbs in Paragraph 2 and to past-tense verbs in Paragraph 3.

Paragraph 1: Mixed Tenses

Paul is different, but everyone liked him. He wears black jeans and a black tee-shirt to class every day. His shoes and socks were black, too. Even his hair is dyed black! I do not understand why he dressed in black. Paul was smart, and he plays soccer better than anyone. Everybody laughs at his funny jokes in class. Even our teacher likes him because he has always acted courteous and nice to everyone. Today, Paul moves to another town. We wish him good luck and said good-by, but we miss him already.

Paragraph 2: Present Tense

Paul _____ different, but everyone _____ him. He _____ black jeans and a black tee-shirt to class every day. His shoes and socks _____ black, too. Even his hair _____ _____ black! I _____ not _____ why he _____ in black. Paul _____ smart, and he _____ soccer better than anyone. Everybody _____ at his funny jokes in class. Even our teacher _____ him because he _____ always _____ courteous and nice to everyone. Today, Paul _____ to another town. We _____ him good luck and _____ good-by, but we _____ him already.

Paragraph 3: Past Tense

Paul _____ different, but everyone _____ him. He _____ black jeans and a black tee-shirt to class every day. His shoes and socks _____ black, too. Even his hair _____ _____ black! I _____ not _____ why he _____ in black. Paul _____ smart, and he _____ soccer better than anyone. Everybody _____ at his funny jokes in class. Even our teacher _____ him because he _____ always _____ courteous and nice to everyone. Today, Paul _____ to another town. We _____ him good luck and _____ good-by, but we _____ him already.

▶ **Exercise 6:** Answer the questions below.

1. What are the three helping verbs for the emphatic form? _____

2. What is the special ending for the main verb in the progressive form? _____

3. What are the future-tense helping verbs? _____

4. What are the past-tense helping verbs? _____

5. What are the present-tense helping verbs? _____

Complete this homework assignment.

1. Write **Present Tense** beside Number 1 and list the present-tense helping verbs. Write **Past Tense** beside Number 2 and list the past-tense helping verbs. Write **Future Tense** beside Number 3 and list the future-tense helping verbs.

   Present Tense: _____, _____, _____, _____, _____, _____, _____

   Past Tense: _____, _____, _____, _____, _____

   Future tense: _____, _____

2. What are the three helping verbs for the emphatic form? _____, _____, _____

3. What is the special ending for the main verb in the progressive form? _____

4. For each sentence, do four things. (1) Underline the verb or verb phrase. (2) Identify the verb tense by writing **1** for present tense, **2** for past tense, or **3** for future tense. (3) Write the past-tense form. (4) Write **R** for Regular or **I** for Irregular.

	Verb Tense	Main Verb Past Tense Form	R or I
1. Aunt Cassie buys family pictures every January.			
2. Rebecca and her mother shopped in Winston for shoes.			
3. Alexander will ride to swimming lessons with us.			

5. Write the sentences below. Underline the verb or verb phrase in each sentence. Then, indicate the voice of the verbs by putting an **A** (active) or **P** (passive) before each sentence.

   _____ 1. The apples were picked by migrant workers.

   _____ 2. Marjorie gasped for air.

   _____ 3. She dyed her hair bright orange.

   _____ 4. The race was won by a Swedish cyclist.

6. Write the four principal parts of the following verbs: **talk** and **run**.

PRESENT	PAST	PAST PARTICIPLE	PRESENT PARTICIPLE
1._____	3._____	5. (**has**) _____	7. (**is**) _____
2._____	4._____	6. (**has**) _____	8. (**is**) _____

7. Conjugate the verb listed below.

Verb Conjugation	Present	Past	Future	Present Perfect	Past Perfect	Future Perfect
For the irregular verb: **write**						

SHURLEY ENGLISH

Notes: _____

_____

_____

_____

_____

_____

_____

_____

_____

_____

_____

_____

_____

_____

_____

_____

_____

_____

_____

_____

_____

_____

_____

_____

_____

_____

_____

_____

_____

_____

Chapter 14 Checkup 44

Name:_____ Date:_____

GRAMMAR

▶ **Exercise 1:** Classify each sentence.

1. _____ Will you give Katherine a message from Kevin before noon?

2. _____ Sometimes, my grandparents and I burn candles during an electrical outage.

3. _____ Mercy! Our new truck was stolen during the middle of the night from our driveway!

SKILLS

▶ **Exercise 2:** Underline the verb or verb phrase in each of these sentences. Then, indicate the voice of the verbs in each sentence by putting an **A** (active) or **P** (passive) in the blank before each sentence.

_____ 1. The packages were unloaded onto the outside dock.

_____ 2. The mockingbird imitated the sound of a cat.

_____ 3. We signed our names at the bottom of the contract.

_____ 4. The pedestrian was stopped by the traffic light at the corner.

▶ **Exercise 3:** Change the underlined mixed-tense verbs in Paragraph 1 to past-tense verbs in Paragraph 2.

Paragraph 1: Mixed Tenses

Nervously, I <u>paced</u> the floor. I <u>join</u> the drama club two years ago. I <u>have acted</u> in three plays but never <u>get</u> the starring role. The director always <u>names</u> somebody else. As she <u>explains</u> it, she <u>judged</u> us on many points. She <u>hates</u> to disappoint anybody, but she <u>picks</u> the best actor for the role. With each play, I <u>gained</u> confidence, but I <u>worry</u> more each time. When she <u>sees</u> that I <u>was</u> nervous, she <u>touches</u> my shoulder. She <u>smiled</u>. I <u>know</u> then that the lead, this time, <u>is</u> mine!

Paragraph 2: Past Tense

Nervously, I _____ the floor. I _____ the drama club two years ago. I _____ _____ in three plays but never _____ the starring role. The director always _____ somebody else. As she _____ it, she _____ us on many points. She _____ to disappoint anybody, but she _____ the best actor for the role. With each play, I _____ confidence, but I _____ more each time. When she _____ that I _____ nervous, she _____ my shoulder. She _____. I _____ then that the lead, this time, _____ mine!

▶ **Exercise 4:** Answer the questions below.

1. What are the three helping verbs for the emphatic form? _____

2. What is the special ending for the main verb in the progressive form? _____

3. What are the present-tense helping verbs? _____

4. What are the past-tense helping verbs? _____

5. What are the future-tense helping verbs? _____

Notes: _____

_____

_____

_____

_____

_____

_____

_____

_____

_____

_____

_____

_____

_____

_____

_____

_____

_____

_____

_____

_____

_____

_____

_____

_____

_____

_____

_____

_____

Classroom Practice 45

Name: _____   Date: _____

INDEPENDENT PRACTICE & REVISED SENTENCES

1. Write a Practice Sentence according to the labels you choose.
Use the SN/SP, V-t, IO DO as your main labels. You may use the other labels in any order and as many times as you wish in order to make a Practice Sentence.
Chapter 14 labels for a Practice Sentence: SN/SP, V-t, IO DO, Adj, Adv, A, P, OP, PPA, C, HV, I, PNA

2. Write a Revised Sentence. Use the following revision strategies: *synonym (syn), antonym (ant), word change (wc), added word (add), deleted word (delete),* or *no change (nc).* Under each word, write the abbreviation of the revision strategy you use.

Labels:

Practice:

Revised:

Strategies:

Labels:

Practice:

Revised:

Strategies:

Labels:

Practice:

Revised:

Strategies:

SHURLEY ENGLISH

Notes: _____

_____

_____

_____

_____

_____

_____

_____

_____

_____

_____

_____

_____

_____

_____

_____

_____

_____

_____

_____

_____

_____

_____

_____

_____

_____

_____

_____

Chapter 15 Writing Evaluation Guide

Name:_____ Date:_____

ROUGH DRAFT CHECK

_____ 1. Did you write your rough draft in pencil?

_____ 2. Did you write the correct headings on the first seven lines of your paper?

_____ 3. Did you use extra wide margins and skip every other line?

_____ 4. Did you write a title at the end of your rough draft?

_____ 5. Did you place your edited rough draft in your Rough Draft folder?

REVISING CHECK

_____ 6. Did you identify the purpose, type of writing, and audience?

_____ 7. Did you check for a topic, topic sentence, and sentences supporting the topic?

_____ 8. Did you check sentences for the right order, and did you combine, rearrange, or delete sentences when necessary?

_____ 9. Did you check for a variety of simple, compound, and complex sentences?

_____ 10. Did you check for any left out, repeated, or unnecessary words?

_____ 11. Did you check for the best choice of words by replacing or deleting unclear words?

_____ 12. Did you check the content for interest and creativity?

_____ 13. Did you check the voice to make sure the writing says what you want it to say?

EDITING CHECK

_____ 14. Did you indent each paragraph?

_____ 15. Did you put an end mark at the end of every sentence?

_____ 16. Did you capitalize the first word of every sentence?

_____ 17. Did you check for all other capitalization mistakes?

_____ 18. Did you check for all punctuation mistakes?
(commas, periods, apostrophes, quotation marks, underlining)

_____ 19. Did you check for misspelled words and for incorrect homonym choices?

_____ 20. Did you check for incorrect spellings of plural and possessive forms?

_____ 21. Did you check for correct construction and punctuation of your sentences?

_____ 22. Did you check for usage mistakes? _(subject/verb agreement, a/an choices, contractions, verb tenses, pronoun/antecedent agreement, pronoun cases, degrees of adjectives, double negatives, etc.)_

_____ 23. Did you put your revised and edited paper in the Rough Draft folder?

FINAL PAPER CHECK

_____ 24. Did you write the final paper in pencil?

_____ 25. Did you center the title on the top line and center your name under the title?

_____ 26. Did you skip a line before starting the writing assignment?

_____ 27. Did you single-space, use wide margins, and write the final paper neatly?

_____ 28. Did you staple your papers in this order: final paper on top, rough draft in the middle, and prewriting map on the bottom? Did you put them in the Final Paper folder?

Notes: _____

Classroom Practice 46

Name:_____ Date:_____

GRAMMAR

▶ **Exercise 1:** Classify each sentence.

1. _____ A thesaurus is a book of synonyms and antonyms.

2. _____ Horrors! That unusual cloud in the western sky is a tornado!

3. _____ The little boy in the yellow cap near the door is a computer whiz.

▶ **Exercise 2:** Use Sentence 3 above to complete the table below.

List the Noun Used	List the Noun Job	Singular or Plural	Common or Proper	Simple Subject	Simple Predicate

SKILLS

▶ **Exercise 3:** Underline the verb or verb phrase in each of these sentences. Then, indicate the voice of the verbs in each sentence by putting an **A** (active) or **P** (passive) in the blank before each sentence.

_____ 1. The falling star made its sudden descent to Earth.

_____ 2. The sheep were herded to a new pasture by a young shepherd.

_____ 3. The prize-winning kite was flown by Amber Hargrove.

_____ 4. Zebras eat leaves from lower branches of deciduous trees.

_____ 5. Pictures of various zoo animals were displayed by local kindergarteners.

▶ **Exercise 4:** Write the four principal parts of the following verbs: **sign** and **ride**.

_____ _____ _____ _____

_____ _____ _____ _____

▶ **Exercise 5:** Conjugate the verb listed below.

Verb Conjugation	Present	Past	Future	Present Perfect	Past Perfect	Future Perfect
For the irregular verb: **grow**						

▶ **Exercise 6:** List the present-tense and past-tense helping verbs in the blanks below.

Present Tense	1.	2.	3.	4.	5.	6.	7.
Past Tense	1.	2.	3.	4.	5.		

▶ **Exercise 7:** Write **R** for regular or **I** for irregular. Then, write the past-tense form.

1. listen_____ **Past tense:** _____   2. pay _____ **Past tense:** _____   3. tear _____ **Past tense:** _____

Notes: _____

_____

_____

_____

_____

_____

_____

_____

_____

_____

_____

_____

_____

_____

_____

_____

_____

_____

_____

_____

_____

_____

_____

_____

_____

_____

_____

_____

_____

_____

Classroom Practice 47

Name:_____ Date:_____

GRAMMAR

▶ **Exercise 1:** Classify each sentence.

1. _____ Amethyst is another name for an expensive purple quartz.

2. _____ My! That attractive girl by the counter in the red jumpsuit is she!

3. _____ My brother's surprise gift from his buddies was a certificate for a dozen cheeseburgers.

SKILLS AND EDITING

▶ **Exercise 2:** Edit the sentences below. **Editing Guide: End Marks: 8 Capitals: 14 Commas: 15**
Quotation Marks: 12 Underlined Explanatory Words: 4 Periods: 4

1. mr russell would you care for dessert brian the head waiter asked politely

2. brian the head waiter asked politely mr russell would you care for dessert

3. mr russell brian the head waiter asked politely would you care for dessert

4. mr russell would you care for dessert brian the head waiter asked politely we have a

   wonderful selection in fact the special for the day is hot peach cobbler with ice cream

SKILLS AND EDITING

▶ **Exercise 3:** Edit the sentences below. **Editing Guide: End Marks: 7 Capitals: 30 Commas: 4**
Apostrophes: 1 Quotation Marks: 10 Underlined Explanatory Words: 4

1. holly exclaimed erica and i are going to steamboat springs in colorado to snowboard

2. erica and i are going to steamboat springs in colorado to snowboard exclaimed holly

3. erica and i holly exclaimed are going to steamboat springs in colorado to snowboard

4. holly exclaimed erica and i are going to steamboat springs in colorado to snowboard

   do you think paula and penny could go with us its during our christmas break in december

Notes: _____

_____

_____

_____

_____

_____

_____

_____

_____

_____

_____

_____

_____

_____

_____

_____

_____

_____

_____

_____

_____

_____

_____

_____

_____

_____

_____

_____

_____

_____

Complete this homework assignment.

1. Rewrite the sentences below, using the Quotation Rules to help you capitalize and punctuate each sentence correctly. Underline the explanatory words.

1. mike twirled around the room and shouted my dad and i are going for a ride in

   a hot air balloon

2. my dad and i are going for a ride in a hot air balloon mike shouted as he twirled

   around the room

3. my dad and i mike shouted excitedly are going for a ride in a hot air balloon

4. my dad and i are going for a ride in a hot air balloon mike shouted excitedly we leave

   this weekend and we wont be back until monday this will be my dream come true

2. Write the four principal parts of the following verbs: **type** and **ring**.

   _____   _____   _____   _____

   _____   _____   _____   _____

3. Conjugate the verbs listed below.

Verb Conjugation	Present	Past	Future	Present Perfect	Past Perfect	Future Perfect
For the regular verb: **organize**						
For the irregular verb: **teach**						

SHURLEY ENGLISH

Notes:

Classroom Practice 50

Name: _____ Date: _____

INDEPENDENT PRACTICE & REVISED SENTENCES

1. Write a Practice Sentence according to the labels you choose.
Use the SN/SP, LV, PrN as your main labels. You may use the other labels in any order and as many times as you wish in order to make a Practice Sentence.
Chapter 16 labels for a Practice Sentence: SN/SP, LV, PrN, Adj, Adv, A, P, OP, PPA, C, HV, I, PNA

2. Write a Revised Sentence. Use the following revision strategies: *synonym (syn), antonym (ant), word change (wc), added word (add), deleted word (delete),* or *no change (nc).* Under each word, write the abbreviation of the revision strategy you use.

Labels:

Practice:

Revised:

Strategies:

Labels:

Practice:

Revised:

Strategies:

Labels:

Practice:

Revised:

Strategies:

Notes: _____

_____

_____

_____

_____

_____

_____

_____

_____

_____

_____

_____

_____

_____

_____

_____

_____

_____

_____

_____

_____

_____

_____

_____

_____

_____

_____

_____

_____

_____

_____

Chapter 17 Writing Evaluation Guide

Name:_____ Date:_____

ROUGH DRAFT CHECK

_____ 1. Did you write your rough draft in pencil?

_____ 2. Did you write the correct headings on the first seven lines of your paper?

_____ 3. Did you use extra wide margins and skip every other line?

_____ 4. Did you write a title at the end of your rough draft?

_____ 5. Did you place your edited rough draft in your Rough Draft folder?

REVISING CHECK

_____ 6. Did you identify the purpose, type of writing, and audience?

_____ 7. Did you check for a topic, topic sentence, and sentences supporting the topic?

_____ 8. Did you check sentences for the right order, and did you combine, rearrange, or delete sentences when necessary?

_____ 9. Did you check for a variety of simple, compound, and complex sentences?

_____ 10. Did you check for any left out, repeated, or unnecessary words?

_____ 11. Did you check for the best choice of words by replacing or deleting unclear words?

_____ 12. Did you check the content for interest and creativity?

_____ 13. Did you check the voice to make sure the writing says what you want it to say?

EDITING CHECK

_____ 14. Did you indent each paragraph?

_____ 15. Did you put an end mark at the end of every sentence?

_____ 16. Did you capitalize the first word of every sentence?

_____ 17. Did you check for all other capitalization mistakes?

_____ 18. Did you check for all punctuation mistakes?
(*commas, periods, apostrophes, quotation marks, underlining*)

_____ 19. Did you check for misspelled words and for incorrect homonym choices?

_____ 20. Did you check for incorrect spellings of plural and possessive forms?

_____ 21. Did you check for correct construction and punctuation of your sentences?

_____ 22. Did you check for usage mistakes? (*subject/verb agreement, a/an choices, contractions, verb tenses, pronoun/antecedent agreement, pronoun cases, degrees of adjectives, double negatives, etc.*)

_____ 23. Did you put your revised and edited paper in the Rough Draft folder?

FINAL PAPER CHECK

_____ 24. Did you write the final paper in pencil?

_____ 25. Did you center the title on the top line and center your name under the title?

_____ 26. Did you skip a line before starting the writing assignment?

_____ 27. Did you single-space, use wide margins, and write the final paper neatly?

_____ 28. Did you staple your papers in this order: final paper on top, rough draft in the middle, and prewriting map on the bottom? Did you put them in the Final Paper folder?

Notes: _____

_____

_____

_____

_____

_____

_____

_____

_____

_____

_____

_____

_____

_____

_____

_____

_____

_____

_____

_____

_____

_____

_____

_____

_____

_____

_____

_____

_____

_____

_____

Classroom Practice 51

Name:_____ Date:_____

GRAMMAR

▶ **Exercise 1:** Classify each sentence.

1. _____ The unfamiliar cat on the porch looked thin and hungry.

2. _____ This new digital camera in the display case is very expensive.

3. _____ Our dinner portions at the sports banquet were quite modest.

SKILLS

▶ **Exercise 2:** Identify the pronoun case by writing **S** for subjective, **O** for objective, or **P** for possessive in the blank. Underline the correct pronoun in parentheses.

_____ 1. Baxter, my dog, barked happily at (I, me).   _____ 5. Will Trina give (I, me) a copy of her notes?

_____ 2. As a present, Jason detailed (my, me) car.   _____ 6. Give applause to (we, our) graduates.

_____ 3. The nursing students were Eric and (I, me).   _____ 7. (They, Them) are dependable vehicles.

_____ 4. Haley and (he, him) live in Jackson.   _____ 8. Buy your supplies from (we, us).

EDITING

▶ **Exercise 3:** Edit the story below. **Total Mistakes: 65**

mmm whats that most wonderful smell exclaimed cindy as she waltzed into the kitchen

that smell happens to be my special homemade chocolate chip cookies replied her brother

spencer my sweet chef said cindy you made my favorite cookies may i please have some

these cookies are going to cost you said spencer as he gleefully waved the plate of warm

chocolate chip cookies under his sisters nose

oh you make me so mad glared cindy all right what do you think theyre worth

spencer said triumphantly you can have all these cookies if you and mark will take me along

when you go to the movies tonight

done cried cindy as she reached blissfully for the plate of cookies this is so totally worth it

SHURLEY ENGLISH

Notes: _____

_____

_____

_____

_____

_____

_____

_____

_____

_____

_____

_____

_____

_____

_____

_____

_____

_____

_____

_____

_____

_____

_____

_____

_____

_____

_____

_____

Classroom Practice 52

Name:_____ Date:_____

GRAMMAR

▶ **Exercise 1:** Classify each sentence.

1. _____ His brother's journey was terribly difficult.

2. _____ The yellow tape was too sticky for the children in my classroom.

3. _____ Yesterday, my sister's scissors were too dull for paper or yarn.

▶ **Exercise 2:** Use Sentence 2 above to complete the table below.

List the Noun Used	List the Noun Job	Singular or Plural	Common or Proper	Simple Subject	Simple Predicate

SKILLS

▶ **Exercise 3:** Complete the table. Then, underline the pronoun in parentheses that agrees with its antecedent.

Pronoun-Antecedent Agreement	Antecedent	S or P	Pronoun S or P
1. The owner of the canoe is (I, we).			
2. Sara and James painted (his, their) fence.			
3. A customer returned (his, their) purchases.			
4. Maria had a question for (her, their) teacher.			
5. Dustin's snake escaped from (its, their) cage.			

▶ **Exercise 4:** Identify the pronoun case by writing **S** for subjective, **O** for objective, or **P** for possessive in the blank. Underline the correct pronoun in parentheses.

____ 1. (We, Us) are committed to finish the project.

____ 2. Kyle consulted (she, her) about his health.

____ 3. The losers were Kristina and (I, me).

____ 4. Dad read to Joe and (I, me) as children.

____ 5. (He, Him) finished semester tests early.

____ 6. The Smiths are not at (they, their) house.

EDITING

▶ **Exercise 5:** Edit the story below. **Total Mistakes: 38**

how did your first day of school go dear asked jennys mom as she gave her daughter a brownie

mom i just cant go back i had a horrible day everyone hates me wailed jenny to her mom

now now dear said jennys mom it will be better tomorrow the first day of teaching is always tough

Notes: _____

_____

_____

_____

_____

_____

_____

_____

_____

_____

_____

_____

_____

_____

_____

_____

_____

_____

_____

_____

_____

_____

_____

_____

_____

_____

_____

_____

_____

_____

Classroom Practice 53, Part A

Name:_____ Date:_____

GRAMMAR

▶ **Exercise 1:** Classify each sentence.

1. _____ My grandmother happily knitted me a warm sweater and scarf.

2. _____ Marcus suddenly made an outstanding discovery in his science lab!

3. _____ The school library is full of interesting books and magazines.

4. _____ My best friend is an excellent actor and an accomplished playwright.

5. _____ The soccer team from Brazil ran eagerly onto the field for practice.

▶ **Exercise 2:** Use Sentence 5 above to complete the table below.

List the Noun Used	List the Noun Job	Singular or Plural	Common or Proper	Simple Subject	Simple Predicate

▶ **Exercise 3:** Write only the pattern number in the blank. Use these patterns:
P1 SN V   P2 SN V-t DO   P3 SN V-t IO DO   P4 SN LV PrN   P5 SN LV PA

_____ 1. These math problems are very easy for me.

_____ 2. Donny returned to camp with a load of firewood.

_____ 3. Woody was our local banker for many years.

_____ 4. Those coupons saved me several dollars on my grocery bill.

_____ 5. Vanessa plays the trombone in her school's marching band.

_____ 6. Two soldiers in my outfit recently became corporals.

_____ 7. The accident blocked traffic at the busy intersection for several hours.

_____ 8. The long voyage has been boring and dull.

_____ 9. The tornado left a horrific path of destruction in my cousin's town.

_____ 10. Ms. Collins showed the investigator an error in his report.

_____ 11. The best mathematicians in our class are you and Beth.

_____ 12. The old yellow bus traveled slowly through the neighborhood.

_____ 13. Mom's Sunday dinner always tastes delicious.

SHURLEY ENGLISH

Classroom Practice 53, Part B

Name:_____ Date:_____

SKILLS

▶ **Exercise 4:** Complete the table. Then, underline the correct verb. **N/Pro** means to identify the subject as a noun or pronoun. Use **S** for singular and **P** for plural.

Indefinite Pronouns and Subject-Verb Agreement	Subject	N/Pro	S or P	Verb S or P
1. Both of the boys (is, are) on the team.				
2. Some of the icing (was, were) smeared on the cake.				
3. Many choices (was, were) available in the store.				
4. Many (has, have) personal cell phones.				
5. Each of the cheerleaders (does, do) aerobics.				
6. Everybody (wants, want) a vacation in August.				
7. No one (was, were) answering the phone.				
8. Several of the committee members (is, are) absent.				
9. Several members (votes, vote) for their favorites.				
10. None of the dessert (was, were) chocolate.				

▶ **Exercise 5:** Complete the table. Then, underline the pronoun in parentheses that agrees with its antecedent.

Pronoun-Antecedent Agreement	Antecedent	S or P	Pronoun S or P
1. The president of the organization is (he, they).			
2. The medical students took (his, their) exam.			
3. A firefighter put on (his, their) mask and gloves.			
4. The technician used (her, their) new equipment.			
5. Keith and Beth waited for (his, their) turn.			
6. Dana's cat cut (its, their) paw on a broken glass.			
7. Scientists finished (his, their) work in November.			
8. A gorilla stared sullenly at (its, their) food.			
9. Justin parked (his, their) bike in the bicycle rack.			
10. Bo and Ben plotted how to trick (their, his) friend.			

▶ **Exercise 6:** Identify the pronoun case by writing **S** for subjective, **O** for objective, or **P** for possessive in the blank. Underline the correct pronoun in parentheses.

_____ 1. (We, Us) identified insects in science.

_____ 2. We admired (she, her) oil paintings.

_____ 3. Joseph volunteered (I, me) for clean-up duty.

_____ 4. The usher found better seats for (they, them).

_____ 5. (She, Her) is the candidate to support.

_____ 6. Study (you, your) vocabulary words.

_____ 7. (He and I, Him and me) are leaving now.

_____ 8. (They, Them) drive to Dallas for work.

_____ 9. Get (he and I, him and me) extra tickets.

_____ 10. Jan likes to visit (he, his) relatives.

Homework 8

1. Write **S** for subjective, **O** for objective, or **P** for possessive. Then, underline the correct pronoun in parentheses.

_____ 1. (He and I, Him and me) are in the same class.

_____ 2. Andrea confided in (I, me) about her new job.

_____ 3. (Me, My) counselor helped me pick classes.

_____ 4. Janet bought (we, our) dinner last night.

_____ 5. Lee showed (she and I, her and me) the photos.

_____ 6. The contestants for the show are (them, they).

2. Complete the table. Then, underline the correct pronoun in the parentheses that agrees with its antecedent.

Pronoun-Antecedent Agreement	Antecedent	S or P	Pronoun S or P
1. The husky puppy yapped at (its, their) mother.			
2. A flight attendant handled (her, their) own luggage.			
3. Several employees earned (his, their) promotions.			

3. Complete the table. Then, underline the correct verb. **N/Pro** means to identify the subject as a noun or pronoun. Use **S** for singular and **P** for plural.

Indefinite Pronouns and Subject-Verb Agreement	Subject	N/Pro	S or P	Verb S or P
1. Someone in the room (has, have) ordered pizza.				
2. The prize (was, were) a gift certificate for fast food.				
3. Many of the prizes (was, were) given away.				

4. Write the four principal parts of the following verbs: **match** and **buy**.

_____ _____ _____ _____

_____ _____ _____ _____

5. Conjugate the verbs listed below.

Verb Conjugation	Present	Past	Future	Present Perfect	Past Perfect	Future Perfect
For the regular verb: **travel**						
For the irregular verb: **ride**						

Notes: _____

_____

_____

_____

_____

_____

_____

_____

_____

_____

_____

_____

_____

_____

_____

_____

_____

_____

_____

_____

_____

_____

_____

_____

_____

_____

_____

_____

_____

_____

_____

_____

Chapter 18 Checkup 54

Name:_____ Date:_____

GRAMMAR

▶ **Exercise 1:** Classify each sentence.

1. _____ That perfume smells too strong for me!

2. _____ Andy mourned over the loss of his dear and beloved pet.

3. _____ He became a pilot after graduation from flight school.

4. _____ Several early shoppers eagerly awaited the arrival of the new fall fashions.

5. _____ During our vacation, my grandfather told me funny stories about my father.

SKILLS

▶ **Exercise 2:** Complete the table. Then, underline the pronoun in parentheses that agrees with its antecedent.

Pronoun-Antecedent Agreement	Antecedent	S or P	Pronoun S or P
1. The captain of the drill squad is (she, they).			
2. The students bought (his, their) own supplies.			
3. Skilled nurses shared (her, their) knowledge with us.			
4. My sister moved into (her, their) new apartment.			

▶ **Exercise 3:** Complete the table. Then, underline the correct verb. **N/Pro** means to identify the subject as a noun or pronoun. Use **S** for singular and **P** for plural.

Indefinite Pronouns and Subject-Verb Agreement	Subject	N/Pro	S or P	Verb S or P
1. A few of the horses (is, are) in the corral.				
2. Few people (was, were) interested in the article.				
3. Everybody (has, have) a personal interest in the team.				
4. Some actors (does, do) appear in car commercials.				
5. Half of the garden (has, have) been planted in shrubs.				

▶ **Exercise 4:** Identify the pronoun case by writing **S** for subjective, **O** for objective, or **P** for possessive in the blank. Underline the correct pronoun in parentheses.

_____ 1. (We, Us) visited the planetarium last July.

_____ 2. The shoe store offered (I, me) a sales job.

_____ 3. Jen's family proudly attended (she, her) recital.

_____ 4. (She, Her) typed the report on my computer.

_____ 5. Aunt Jill found the perfect gift for (they, them).

_____ 6. I prefer (you, your) white dress and shoes.

_____ 7. (They, Them) browsed stores for bargains.

_____ 8. (He and I, Him and me) were not skating.

_____ 9. Payton plays (he, his) drums every day.

_____ 10. Look for (he and I, him and me) at the game.

SHURLEY ENGLISH

Notes: _____

_____

_____

_____

_____

_____

_____

_____

_____

_____

_____

_____

_____

_____

_____

_____

_____

_____

_____

_____

_____

_____

_____

_____

_____

_____

_____

Classroom Practice 55

Name: _____ Date: _____

INDEPENDENT PRACTICE & REVISED SENTENCES

1. Write a Practice Sentence according to the labels you choose. Use the SN/SP LV PA as your main labels. You may use the other labels in any order and as many times as you wish in order to make a Practice Sentence.
   Chapter 18 labels for a Practice Sentence: SN/SP, LV, PA, Adj, Adv, A, P, OP, PPA, C, HV, I, PNA

2. Write a Revised Sentence. Use the following revision strategies: *synonym (syn), antonym (ant), word change (wc), added word (add), deleted word (delete), or no change (nc).* Under each word, write the abbreviation of the revision strategy you use.

Labels: _____

Practice: _____

Revised: _____

Strategies: _____

Labels: _____

Practice: _____

Revised: _____

Strategies: _____

Labels: _____

Practice: _____

Revised: _____

Strategies: _____

Notes: _____

_____

_____

_____

_____

_____

_____

_____

_____

_____

_____

_____

_____

_____

_____

_____

_____

_____

_____

_____

_____

_____

_____

_____

_____

_____

_____

_____

_____

_____

_____

Chapter 19 Writing Evaluation Guide

Name:_____ Date:_____

ROUGH DRAFT CHECK

_____ 1. Did you write your rough draft in pencil?

_____ 2. Did you write the correct headings on the first seven lines of your paper?

_____ 3. Did you use extra wide margins and skip every other line?

_____ 4. Did you write a title at the end of your rough draft?

_____ 5. Did you place your edited rough draft in your Rough Draft folder?

REVISING CHECK

_____ 6. Did you identify the purpose, type of writing, and audience?

_____ 7. Did you check for a topic, topic sentence, and sentences supporting the topic?

_____ 8. Did you check sentences for the right order, and did you combine, rearrange, or delete sentences when necessary?

_____ 9. Did you check for a variety of simple, compound, and complex sentences?

_____ 10. Did you check for any left out, repeated, or unnecessary words?

_____ 11. Did you check for the best choice of words by replacing or deleting unclear words?

_____ 12. Did you check the content for interest and creativity?

_____ 13. Did you check the voice to make sure the writing says what you want it to say?

EDITING CHECK

_____ 14. Did you indent each paragraph?

_____ 15. Did you put an end mark at the end of every sentence?

_____ 16. Did you capitalize the first word of every sentence?

_____ 17. Did you check for all other capitalization mistakes?

_____ 18. Did you check for all punctuation mistakes?
(commas, periods, apostrophes, quotation marks, underlining)

_____ 19. Did you check for misspelled words and for incorrect homonym choices?

_____ 20. Did you check for incorrect spellings of plural and possessive forms?

_____ 21. Did you check for correct construction and punctuation of your sentences?

_____ 22. Did you check for usage mistakes? *(subject/verb agreement, a/an choices, contractions, verb tenses, pronoun/antecedent agreement, pronoun cases, degrees of adjectives, double negatives, etc.)*

_____ 23. Did you put your revised and edited paper in the Rough Draft folder?

FINAL PAPER CHECK

_____ 24. Did you write the final paper in pencil?

_____ 25. Did you center the title on the top line and center your name under the title?

_____ 26. Did you skip a line before starting the writing assignment?

_____ 27. Did you single-space, use wide margins, and write the final paper neatly?

_____ 28. Did you staple your papers in this order: final paper on top, rough draft in the middle, and prewriting map on the bottom? Did you put them in the Final Paper folder?

SHURLEY ENGLISH

Notes: _____

Classroom Practice 56

Name:_____ Date:_____

GRAMMAR

▶ **Exercise 1:** Classify each sentence.

1. _____ That new movie made him successful.

2. _____ We thought it a wonderful view during sunset.

3. _____ The President appointed him general.

4. _____ The dye in the sink colored the white shirt a pale blue.

SKILLS

▶ **Exercise 2:** Complete the table. Then, underline the pronoun in parentheses that agrees with its antecedent.

Pronoun-Antecedent Agreement	Antecedent	S or P	Pronoun S or P
1. The raccoon washed (its, their) food in the stream.			
2. The twins learned to brush (her, their) teeth.			
3. Butterflies began (its, their) trip south for winter.			
4. Wiley hunted for (his, their) souvenirs in the bag.			

▶ **Exercise 3:** Complete the table. Then, underline the correct verb. **N/Pro** means to identify the subject as a noun or pronoun. Use **S** for singular and **P** for plural.

Indefinite Pronouns and Subject-Verb Agreement	Subject	N/Pro	S or P	Verb S or P
1. Some of the cashiers (has, have) been trained.				
2. Few (has, have) qualified for promotion.				
3. Anyone (is, are) allowed to study in this room.				
4. None of the pasta (is, are) on the buffet.				
5. Some (needs, need) more time for their project.				

▶ **Exercise 4:** Identify the pronoun case by writing **S** for subjective, **O** for objective, or **P** for possessive in the blank. Underline the correct pronoun in parentheses.

_____ 1. (We, Us) painted Sharon's kitchen bright red.

_____ 2. Pam consulted (us, we) about babysitting.

_____ 3. (She, Her) planned a long vacation to Canada.

_____ 4. Mimi cooked sweet potatoes for (he, him).

_____ 5. Other students gave (she, her) extra help.

_____ 6. (You, Your) oak trees will need trimming soon.

_____ 7. (They, Them) visited the convention center.

_____ 8. I knocked on (they, their) door this morning.

_____ 9. (He and I, Him and me) learned to fish.

_____10. Listen to (she and I, her and me) sing for you.

Notes: _____

_____

_____

_____

_____

_____

_____

_____

_____

_____

_____

_____

_____

_____

_____

_____

_____

_____

_____

_____

_____

_____

_____

_____

_____

_____

_____

_____

_____

_____

_____

Classroom Practice 57

Name:_____ Date:_____

GRAMMAR

▶ **Exercise 1:** Classify each sentence.

1. _____ The hot weather turned the trees brown.

2. _____ We consider my grandfather a great and honorable man.

3. _____ My friends and I painted my bedroom green and purple.

4. _____ My mother and father consider my brother an excellent artist.

SKILLS

▶ **Exercise 2:** Write the four demonstrative pronouns in the correct column in the chart below.

SINGULAR, NEAR	PLURAL, NEAR	SINGULAR, FAR	PLURAL, FAR
1. _____	2. _____	3. _____	4. _____

▶ **Exercise 3:** Each underlined word is a demonstrative pronoun or adjective and is singular or plural. Underline the correct choices. If the word has an antecedent, write it in the blank; otherwise, write **no**.

1. <u>This</u> is the way to the skate park.　　(Dem Pro, Dem Adj) (Singular, Plural)　　(Antecedent _____)

2. <u>This</u> way is to the skate park.　　(Dem Pro, Dem Adj) (Singular, Plural)　　(Antecedent _____)

▶ **Exercise 4:** Underline the correct demonstrative pronoun and write its antecedent in the blank. Then, underline the correct verb.

1. (This, These) (is, are) my tickets for the balcony section.　　(Antecedent _____)

2. (This, These) (is, are) my ticket to the balcony section.　　(Antecedent _____)

▶ **Exercise 5:** Indicate whether the word in bold is an interrogative pronoun or an interrogative adjective by underlining the correct answer in parentheses.

1. **What** were the names of the committee members?　　(Int Pro, Int Adj)

2. On **what** aisle will I find the printer cartridges?　　(Int Pro, Int Adj)

▶ **Exercise 6:** Underline the correct interrogative pronoun for each sentence below.

1. (Who, Whom) requested this safety report?　　2. The safety report was requested by (who, whom)?

3. (Who, Whom) will you ask to the party?

▶ **Exercise 7:** Conjugate the verbs listed below.

Verb Conjugation	Present	Past	Future	Present Perfect	Past Perfect	Future Perfect
For the regular verb: **design**						
For the irregular verb: **teach**						

Notes: _____

_____

_____

_____

_____

_____

_____

_____

_____

_____

_____

_____

_____

_____

_____

_____

_____

_____

_____

_____

_____

_____

_____

_____

_____

_____

_____

_____

_____

_____

_____

_____

Classroom Practice 58, Part A

Name:_____ Date:_____

GRAMMAR

▶ **Exercise 1:** Classify each sentence.

1. _____ The music teacher taught me a new song for the recital.

2. _____ The waiter put fresh flowers in the vases on the tables.

3. _____ Jamie painted her sign bright red for the parade.

4. _____ Mark and Paula are extremely helpful today.

5. _____ My children named the large gorilla at the zoo Big Ugly.

6. _____ My friends' holiday in the Bahamas ended quite abruptly.

7. _____ Vanessa was captain of the cheerleaders during her senior year.

▶ **Exercise 2:** Use Sentence 7 above to complete the table below.

List the Noun Used	List the Noun Job	Singular or Plural	Common or Proper	Simple Subject	Simple Predicate

▶ **Exercise 3:** Write only the pattern number in the blank. Use these patterns:
P1 SN V   P2 SN V-t DO   P3 SN V-t IO DO   P4 SN LV PrN
P5 SN LV PA   P6 SN V-t DO OCN   P7 SN V-t DO OCA

_____ 1. Molly kept her room spotless.

_____ 2. The competitors felt exhausted after the final race.

_____ 3. The meteorologist predicted more rain today.

_____ 4. Did Sally's classmates vote her queen of the prom?

_____ 5. The winner of the first race was he.

_____ 6. The market in town has fabulous fresh seafood daily.

_____ 7. April brought us a variety of flowers from her garden.

_____ 8. The majority of the players considered practice very helpful.

_____ 9. Birds usually migrate in the spring and fall.

_____ 10. This food and clothing are gifts for children in the war-torn province.

_____ 11. Did you consider him the winner in the last game?

SHURLEY ENGLISH

Classroom Practice 58, Part B

Name:_____ Date:_____

SKILLS

▶ **Exercise 4:** Write a reflexive or intensive pronoun in the first blank. Write R or I in the second blank to identify the pronoun as reflexive or intensive.

1. We _____ are the best team. _____   3. I wanted the chocolate pie for _____. _____

2. The clock _____ was an antique. _____   4. He caught _____ grinning at her. _____

▶ **Exercise 5:** Write the four demonstrative pronouns in the correct column in the chart below.

SINGULAR, NEAR	PLURAL, NEAR	SINGULAR, FAR	PLURAL, FAR
1. _____	2. _____	3. _____	4. _____

▶ **Exercise 6:** Each underlined word is a demonstrative pronoun or adjective and is singular or plural. Underline the correct choices. If the word has an antecedent, write it in the blank; otherwise, write **no**.

1. This highway goes to Galveston, Texas.   (Dem Pro, Dem Adj) (Singular, Plural)   (Antecedent _____)

2. This is the finest collection I've ever seen.   (Dem Pro, Dem Adj) (Singular, Plural)   (Antecedent _____)

▶ **Exercise 7:** Underline the correct demonstrative pronoun and write its antecedent in the blank. Then, underline the correct verb.

1. (That, Those) (is, are) the foundation for the entire building.   (Antecedent _____)

2. (This, These) (is, are) remarkable discoveries for space technology.   (Antecedent _____)

▶ **Exercise 8:** Indicate whether the word in bold is an interrogative pronoun or an interrogative adjective by underlining the correct answer in parentheses.

1. **Which** is your favorite Mexican restaurant?   (Int Pro, Int Adj)

2. In **which** vehicle is the baby's car seat?   (Int Pro, Int Adj)

▶ **Exercise 9:** Underline the correct interrogative pronoun for each sentence below.

1. Jonathan ran errands for (who, whom)?

2. (Who, Whom) parked in the boss's parking space?

3. To (who, whom) did you write a letter?

▶ **Exercise 10:** Conjugate the verbs listed below.

Verb Conjugation	Present	Past	Future	Present Perfect	Past Perfect	Future Perfect
For the regular verb: **search**						
For the irregular verb: **choose**						

Homework 9

1. Underline the correct demonstrative pronoun and write its antecedent in the blank. Then, underline the correct verb.

   1. (That, Those) (is, are) the ladies in your club by the far door. _____

   2. (This, These) (is, are) our classroom. _____

   3. (That, Those) (was, were) my sister's picture in the newspaper. _____

2. Underline the correct interrogative pronoun for each sentence below.

   1. (Who, Whom) gave the order to advance?   3. To (who, whom) did you wish to speak?

   2. The team was coached by (who, whom)?   4. Yesterday (who, whom) heard the shot?

3. Write a reflexive or intensive pronoun in the first blank and write **R** or **I** in the second blank to identify the pronoun as reflexive or intensive.

   1. The instructors _____ missed their early class. _____

   2. Dad chuckled to _____ during the play. _____

   3. The old rifle _____ was in excellent condition. _____

4. Write the four principal parts of the following verbs: **discuss** and **bring**.

   _____   _____   _____   _____

   _____   _____   _____   _____

5. Conjugate the verbs listed below.

Verb Conjugation	Present	Past	Future	Present Perfect	Past Perfect	Future Perfect
For the regular verb: **select**						
For the irregular verb: **sing**						

Notes: _____

Chapter 20 Checkup 59

Name:_____ Date:_____

GRAMMAR

▶ **Exercise 1:** Classify each sentence.

1. _____ A group of campers searched the woods for animal tracks.

2. _____ He gave the contractor the blueprints for the new addition to the library.

3. _____ The fashion critic declared the fashion show a success.

4. _____ The young football players were very strong for their age.

5. _____ The tall, gangling youth in baggy trousers is my best friend's son.

6. _____ The long green worm slowly crept along the smallest branch of the gigantic tree.

7. _____ Many vacationers chose the pyramids of Egypt the best tourist attraction in the world.

▶ **Exercise 2:** Use Sentence 7 above to complete the table below.

List the Noun Used	List the Noun Job	Singular or Plural	Common or Proper	Simple Subject	Simple Predicate

SKILLS

▶ **Exercise 3:** Write a reflexive or intensive pronoun in the first blank. Write **R** or **I** in the second blank to identify the pronoun as reflexive or intensive.

1. The doctor _____ talked to us. _____   3. Lori bought a wool coat for _____. _____

2. We cleaned our own fish _____. _____   4. I found _____ falling asleep. _____

▶ **Exercise 4:** Underline the correct demonstrative pronoun and write its antecedent in the blank. Then, underline the correct verb.

1. (This, These) (is, are) the highest quality carpet in the store.   (Antecedent _____)

2. (That, Those) (is, are) Stacey's favorite silver earrings.   (Antecedent _____)

▶ **Exercise 5:** Indicate whether the word in bold is an interrogative pronoun or an interrogative adjective by underlining the correct answer in parentheses.

1. **Whose** is the red coat in the closet?   (Int Pro, Int Adj)

2. **Whose** coat is the red one in the closet?   (Int Pro, Int Adj)

Notes: _____

Classroom Practice 60

Name: _____   Date: _____

INDEPENDENT PRACTICE & REVISED SENTENCES

1. Write a Practice Sentence according to the labels you choose. Use the SN/SP V-t DO OCN/OCA as your main labels. You may use the other labels in any order and as many times as you wish in order to make a Practice Sentence.
Chapter 20 labels for a Practice Sentence: SN/SP, V-t DO OCN/OCA, Adj, Adv, A, P, OP, PPA, C, HV, I, PNA

2. Write a Revised Sentence. Use the following revision strategies: *synonym (syn), antonym (ant), word change (wc), added word (add), deleted word (delete), or no change (nc).* Under each word, write the abbreviation of the revision strategy you use.

Labels:

Practice:

Revised:

Strategies:

Labels:

Practice:

Revised:

Strategies:

Labels:

Practice:

Revised:

Strategies:

Notes: _____

_____

_____

_____

_____

_____

_____

_____

_____

_____

_____

_____

_____

_____

_____

_____

_____

_____

_____

_____

_____

_____

_____

_____

_____

_____

_____

_____

_____

Classroom Practice 61

Name:_____ Date:_____

GRAMMAR

▶ **Exercise 1:** Write only the pattern number in the blank. Use these patterns:

P1 SN V   P2 SN V-t DO   P3 SN V-t IO DO   P4 SN LV PrN
P5 SN LV PA   P6 SN V-t DO OCN   P7 SN V-t DO OCA

_____ 1. Hand the newspaper to me.

_____ 2. Henry has been ill for two days.

_____ 3. Betty painted her wall green.

_____ 4. We consider him an
excellent dentist.

_____ 5. He sent her a dozen roses!

_____ 6. The pianist played beautifully.

_____ 7. After sunset, the rain became sleet.

SKILLS

▶ **Exercise 2:** Write the different forms for the adjectives and adverbs below.

| RULE 1: Simple form | RULE 2: Comparative form (er, more) | RULE 3: Superlative form (est, most) |

Simple Form	Comparative Form	Superlative Form
1.	better	
2. respectable		
3.		grouchiest
4. delightful		
5.	less (or lesser)	
6. sensible		
7.		worst
8.	more graceful	

▶ **Exercise 3:** In each blank, write the correct form of the adjective or adverb in parentheses to complete the sentence.

1. We just witnessed the _____ magic trick ever! (**incredible**)

2. This whipped icing is _____ than the sugar icing on the other cake. (**creamy**)

3. Tonight, Kendra's performance on the piano was exceptionally _____. (**good**)

4. Jordan scored _____ than I did on the geography test yesterday. (**badly**)

5. Of all the cards, the glossy black business card looks the _____. (**professional**)

EDITING

▶ **Exercise 4:** Edit the story below. **Total Mistakes: 45**

wow wade exclaimed to his brother tim this report on the grand coulee dam is more

interesting than i thought did you know that the grand coulee dam is almost a mile long and it

is taller than the great pyramid of giza

it is also twice as tall as niagara falls and it is the largest concrete structure in the united

states tim replied he laughed as he explained i did a report on the grand coulee dam last year

Notes:

Classroom Practice 62

Name:_____   Date:_____

GRAMMAR

▶ **Exercise 1:** Write only the pattern number in the blank. Use these patterns:

P1 SN V   P2 SN V-t DO   P3 SN V-t IO DO   P4 SN LV PrN
P5 SN LV PA   P6 SN V-t DO OCN   P7 SN V-t DO OCA

_____ 1. We rent land from our neighbor.
_____ 2. She made the pizza crust extra crispy.
_____ 3. The voters elected him senator.
_____ 4. Toby is an industrious employee.

_____ 5. He asked me the same question.
_____ 6. We are going to the science fair.
_____ 7. These new hairstyles are cute.

SKILLS

▶ **Exercise 2:** First, put parentheses around each prepositional phrase. Next, write **Adj** or **Adv** above each phrase to tell whether it is an adjective or adverb phrase. Then, write the word each phrase modifies beside the **Adj** or **Adv** label.

1. The flutist in the symphony orchestra played with great flair.

2. From Alaska, my father wrote many letters to Katie and me.

3. At the hotel in Switzerland, Elaine slept in an antique feather bed.

4. Mary Rose is the soprano singer on the front row.

5. My cousin rode his horse in the Independence Day parade down Main Street.

6. The clown in the funny little car drove around the circus ring.

7. A nurse at the hospital found a Siamese kitten in the parking lot.

▶ **Exercise 3:** Write the different forms for the adjectives and adverbs below.

RULE 1: Simple form	RULE 2: Comparative form (er, more)	RULE 3: Superlative form (est, most)

Simple Form	Comparative Form	Superlative Form
1.	further	
2. crowded		
3.	healthier	

▶ **Exercise 4:** In each blank, write the correct form of the adjective or adverb in parentheses to complete the sentence.

1. This black and white terrier puppy is _____ than the brown and white one. (**spunky**)
2. Chocolate raspberry coffee is the _____ flavor of this month. (**popular**)
3. The Bulldogs played _____ last Friday night. (**well**)

Notes: _____

Classroom Practice 63, Part A

Name:_____ Date:_____

GRAMMAR

▶ **Exercise 1:** Classify each sentence. Underline the complete subject once and the complete predicate twice.

1. _____ The teachers declared the young athletes worthy of a trophy.

2. _____ Terri gave her dad several unusual coins for his collection.

3. _____ The football players voted him captain again.

4. _____ Bismarck is the historic capital of North Dakota.

5. _____ Drain the old oil from your mower at the end of mowing season.

6. _____ The gelatin salad melted on the kitchen counter during the night.

7. _____ The family was enthusiastic and cheerful throughout the whole trip.

▶ **Exercise 2:** Use Sentence 2 above to complete the table below.

List the Noun Used	List the Noun Job	Singular or Plural	Common or Proper	Simple Subject	Simple Predicate

▶ **Exercise 3:** Write only the pattern number in the blank. Use these patterns:

    P1 SN V   P2 SN V-t DO   P3 SN V-t IO DO   P4 SN LV PrN
    P5 SN LV PA   P6 SN V-t DO OCN   P7 SN V-t DO OCA

_____ 1. Her bucket of soapy water spilled across the kitchen floor.

_____ 2. The superintendent named my cousin principal.

_____ 3. Her garden is a showplace of flowers and vegetables.

_____ 4. The chlorine in the pool turned his hair green.

_____ 5. The meteorologist gave us fair warning about the approaching storm.

_____ 6. The bulldozers in the field will dig a massive lake for local fishermen.

_____ 7. The rocks and crevices were tough on my shoes.

SHURLEY ENGLISH

Classroom Practice 63, Part B

Name:_____ Date:_____

SKILLS

▶ **Exercise 4:** First, underline the subject once. Next, write the rule number that applies. Then, write **S** if the subject is singular or **P** if the subject is plural. Finally, underline the verb that agrees with the subject.

AGREEMENT RULES FOR SPECIAL CASES 1: Singular collective nouns (united action) 2: Plural collective nouns (separate actions) 3: Singular noun ending in -s that takes a singular verb. 4: Singular noun ending in -s that takes a plural verb. 5: Titles and groups of words. 6: Amount of money, time, or measurement. 7: Amount or time with plural object of the preposition. 8: Compound subjects with and. 9: Compound subjects with or, nor. 10: Inverted subjects/verbs.

Rule	S/P	
		1. The choir (is attending, are attending) a banquet in their honor at Lewis Hall.
		2. One hundred dollars (is, are) the price for the mountain bike.
		3. Economics (is, are) my older brother's major in college.
		4. Elizabeth and Erica (has, have) bunk beds in their room.
		5. My crew (enjoys, enjoy) different vacation activities with their families.
		6. The Bird Watchers of America (meets, meet) on the last Saturday of each month.
		7. Sixty pounds of potatoes (is, are) more than enough.
		8. Either Mother or the twins (is, are) talking to Grandmother.
		9. Dad's binoculars (gives, give) us a better view from the top of the stadium.
		10. Where (is, are) my ticket to the concert?

▶ **Exercise 5:** First, put parentheses around each prepositional phrase. Next, write **Adj** or **Adv** above each phrase to tell whether it is an adjective or adverb phrase. Then, write the word each phrase modifies beside the **Adj** or **Adv**

1. Some of the teens completed the obstacle course.

2. Everybody in the auditorium stared at the strange-looking costumes.

3. Our dog is a Dalmatian with black spots.

4. One of the highest mountains in the world is Tent Peak in Nepal.

5. The football team is watching a film of the opposing team for next week's game.

▶ **Exercise 6:** In each blank, write the correct form of the adjective or adverb in parentheses to complete the sentence.

1. Your suitcase is _____ than mine is. (**full**)

2. Parker feels _____ than Mason feels. (**ill**)

3. Juanita Torrez is the _____ student in our biology class. (**determined**)

4. The storm yesterday was _____ than the storm last week. (**destructive**)

Classroom Practice 64

Name:_____ Date:_____

GRAMMAR

▶ **Exercise 1:** Write only the pattern number in the blank. Use these patterns: **P1 SN V   P2 SN V-t DO**
P3 SN V-t IO DO   P4 SN LV PrN   P5 SN LV PA   P6 SN V-t DO OCN   P7 SN V-t DO OCA

_____ 1. They considered tea a luxury.
_____ 2. He and I visited with our friends.
_____ 3. Are the new workers lazy?
_____ 4. The jury found him innocent.

_____ 5. My aunt is a famous artist.
_____ 6. Give me a second chance!
_____ 7. We heard sirens in the distance.

SKILLS

▶ **Exercise 2:** For each noun, write the rule number and the plural form that follows the rule. Some nouns have two acceptable plural forms, but you should use the plural spellings that can be verified by the rules below.

1. Add *-s* to *most singular nouns*.
2. Add *-es* to words ending in *ch, sh, z, s, ss, x*.
3. Add *-es* to words ending in *a consonant plus* **o**.
4. Add *-es* to words ending in *a consonant plus* **y**, change **y** to **i** before adding **es**.
5. Add *-es* to words ending in *f* or *fe*; change **f** or **fe** to **v** before adding **es**.

6. Add *-s* to words ending in *f* or *ff*.
7. Add *-s* to words ending in *a vowel plus* **o**.
8. Add *-s* to words ending in *a vowel plus* **y**.
9. *Change the spelling completely for the plural form of some irregular nouns.*
10. *Spell some irregular nouns the same for both the singular and plural forms.*

Noun	Rule	Plural Form	Noun	Rule	Plural Form
1. guess			4. wife		
2. experiment			5. mouse		
3. fish			6. chimney		

▶ **Exercise 3:** First, underline the subject once. Next, write the rule number that applies. Then, write **S** if the subject is singular or **P** if the subject is plural. Finally, underline the verb that agrees with the subject.

AGREEMENT RULES FOR SPECIAL CASES 1: Singular collective nouns (united action) **2:** Plural collective nouns (separate actions) **3:** Singular noun ending in –s that takes a singular verb. **4:** Singular noun ending in –s that takes a plural verb. **5:** Titles and groups of words. **6:** Amount of money, time, or measurement. **7:** Amount or time with plural object of the preposition. **8:** Compound subjects with and. **9:** Compound subjects with or, nor. **10:** Inverted subjects/verbs.

Rule	S/P	
		1. Our family usually (goes, go) on vacation in July.
		2. Sixteen ounces (is, are) a pound.
		3. Civics (is, are) a ninth grade course.

▶ **Exercise 4:** First, put parentheses around each prepositional phrase. Next, write **Adj** or **Adv** above each phrase to tell whether it is an adjective or adverb phrase. Then, write the word each phrase modifies beside the **Adj** or **Adv** label.

1. A few of the ponies are in the stable.

2. The astronauts in the simulator trained for weightlessness.

▶ **Exercise 5:** In each blank, write the correct form of the adjective or adverb in parentheses to complete the sentence.

1. The comedian was the _____ act of the evening. (**entertaining**)

2. Daniel scored _____ on his college entrance test. (**well**)

Homework 10

1. First, put parentheses around each prepositional phrase. Next, write **Adj** or **Adv** above each phrase to tell whether it is an adjective or adverb phrase. Then, write the word each phrase modifies beside the **Adj** or **Adv** label.

The musicians on the stage played loudly for the noisy crowd.

2. First, underline the subject once. Next, write the rule number that applies. Then, write **S** if the subject is singular or **P** if the subject is plural. Finally, underline the verb that agrees with the subject.

> **AGREEMENT RULES FOR SPECIAL CASES** **1:** Singular collective nouns (united action) **2:** Plural collective nouns (separate actions) **3:** Singular noun ending in –s that takes a singular verb. **4:** Singular noun ending in –s that takes a plural verb. **5:** Titles and groups of words. **6:** Amount of money, time, or measurement. **7:** Amount or time with plural object of the preposition. **8:** Compound subjects with and. **9:** Compound subjects with or, nor. **10:** Inverted subjects/verbs.

Rule	S/P	
		1. Athletics (keep, keeps) me in good physical condition.
		2. Forty pounds (is, are) a lot of weight to lose.
		3. The gang (plays, play) cards together every Friday night.
		4. Neither Zack nor Leon (is, are) ready for the camping trip.
		5. Who (was, were) the winner of the science exhibition?
		6. The dance committee (does, do) not agree on a theme for the next dance.
		7. The Three Musketeers (has, have) been made into a movie several times.
		8. A boy and girl (is sitting, are sitting) on the grass under a tree.
		9. Dressy slacks (was, were) appropriate attire for the occasion.
		10. Who (was, were) the performers in the back row?

3. For each noun, write the rule number and the plural form that follows the rule. Some nouns have two acceptable plural forms, but you should use the plural spellings that can be verified by the rules below.

> **RULES FOR MAKING REGULAR NOUNS PLURAL**
> **Add -s to nouns without special endings.**
>   1. most singular nouns.
> **Add -es to nouns with these special endings:**
>   2. *ch, sh, z, s, ss, x.*
>   3. a consonant plus *o.*
>   4. a consonant plus *y,*
>   change **y** to **i** before adding **es.**
>   5. *f* or *fe*, change *f* or *fe* to **v** before adding **es.**
>
> **Add -s to nouns with these special endings:**
>   6. *f* or *ff.*
>   7. a vowel plus *o.*
>   8. a vowel plus *y.*
> **RULES FOR MAKING IRREGULAR NOUNS PLURAL**
>   9. Change the spelling completely for the plural form.
>   10. Spell the same for both the singular and plural form.

Noun	Rule	Plural Form	Noun	Rule	Plural Form
1. sweater			4. deer		
2. patio			5. bench		
3. woman			6. pulley		

4. Conjugate the verbs listed below.

Verb Conjugation	Present	Past	Future	Present Perfect	Past Perfect	Future Perfect
For the regular verb: **estimate**						
For the irregular verb: **become**						

Chapter 22 Checkup 65

Name:_____ Date:_____

GRAMMAR

▶ **Exercise 1:** Write only the pattern number in the blank. Use these patterns: **P1 SN V   P2 SN V-t DO**
P3 SN V-t IO DO   P4 SN LV PrN   P5 SN LV PA   P6 SN V-t DO OCN   P7 SN V-t DO OCA

_____ 1. She served tea at our noon meal.

_____ 2. We liked our tea unsweetened.

_____ 3. I chose him director of our choir.

_____ 4. My father is a surgeon.

_____ 5. He gave them clear directions.

_____ 6. Some turtles nest among tree roots.

_____ 7. We were hungry all day.

SKILLS

▶ **Exercise 2:** For each noun, write the rule number and the plural form that follows the rule. Some nouns have two acceptable plural forms, but you should use the plural spellings that can be verified by the rules below.

> 1. Add *-s* to *most singular nouns.*
> 2. Add *-es* to words ending in *ch, sh, z, s, ss, x.*
> 3. Add *-es* to words ending in *a consonant plus o.*
> 4. Add *-es* to words ending in *a consonant plus y,* change **y** to **i** before adding **es**.
> 5. Add *-es* to words ending in *f* or *fe*; change **f** or **fe** to **v** before adding **es**.
> 6. Add *-s* to words ending in *f or ff.*
> 7. Add *-s* to words ending in *a vowel plus o.*
> 8. Add *-s* to words ending in *a vowel plus y.*
> 9. *Change the spelling completely for the plural form of some irregular nouns.*
> 10. *Spell some irregular nouns the same for both the singular and plural forms.*

Noun	Rule	Plural Form	Noun	Rule	Plural Form
1. dragonfly			4. rodeo		
2. tornado			5. cliff		
3. thorax			6. goose		

▶ **Exercise 3:** First, underline the subject once. Next, write the rule number that applies. Then, write **S** if the subject is singular or **P** if the subject is plural. Finally, underline the verb that agrees with the subject.

> **AGREEMENT RULES FOR SPECIAL CASES 1:** Singular collective nouns (united action) **2:** Plural collective nouns (separate actions) **3:** Singular noun ending in –s that takes a singular verb. **4:** Singular noun ending in –s that takes a plural verb. **5:** Titles and groups of words. **6:** Amount of money, time, or measurement. **7:** Amount or time with plural object of the preposition. **8:** Compound subjects with and. **9:** Compound subjects with or, nor. **10:** Inverted subjects/verbs.

Rule	S/P	
		1. Pliers (is, are) helpful for removing bolts.
		2. (Was, Were) Lorraine the accountant?
		3. *Pirates of the Caribbean* (is, are) a very popular movie this year.

▶ **Exercise 4:** First, put parentheses around each prepositional phrase. Next, write **Adj** or **Adv** above each phrase to tell whether it is an adjective or adverb phrase. Then, write the word each phrase modifies beside the **Adj** or **Adv** label.

1. The conference speaker is a Serbian scientist with experience in microbiology.

2. A basket of fruit and cheese arrived yesterday in the mail.

▶ **Exercise 5:** In each blank, write the correct form of the adjective or adverb in parentheses to complete the sentence.

1. This young gymnastics team is the _____ I have ever seen. (**confident**)

2. Veronica's team played _____ during the regional tournament. (**badly**)

Notes: _____

_____

_____

_____

_____

_____

_____

_____

_____

_____

_____

_____

_____

_____

_____

_____

_____

_____

_____

_____

_____

_____

_____

_____

_____

_____

_____

_____

_____

Classroom Practice 66

Name:_____   Date:_____

SKILLS AND EDITING

Write the capitalization and punctuation corrections only.
Editing Guide: End Marks: 7   Capitals: 23   Commas: 8   Apostrophes: 3

sairaalantie 14

95900 kolari

FINLAND

june 27 20——

dear trey

   lucas and i are spending the summer with our grandparents in finland they are showing

us the sights and we are having a great time

   there is one thing that is very different from the united states it is daylight 24 hours a day

here and its hard to go to bed at night when the sun is shining outside ill e-mail you pictures

and more information as soon as i get my new computer

   since we will be returning the last of august maybe all the cousins could meet at

maggies diner for fried catfish hush puppies and french fries it will be fun to see

everyone again

                                                    your cousin

                                                    ian

Notes: _____

Classroom Practice 67

Name:_____ Date:_____

SKILLS AND EDITING

Write the capitalization and punctuation corrections only.
Editing Guide: End Marks: 8   Capitals: 35   Commas: 7   Periods: 4   Colons: 1

755 sunset drive

springville ut 00006

june 3 20—

mr and mrs dave phillips

829 bridgeford street

springville ut 00006

dear mr and mrs phillips

i am contacting all the families in my neighborhood to let them know that i am providing babysitting services during the summer and on weekends i love children and enjoy doing activities with them

i have my own transportation and i would be happy to baby-sit your children if you need me i will follow all your instructions and will watch your children carefully because i take my job very seriously

i believe you will find me a responsible babysitter since i have been babysitting several years i will be glad to supply references of satisfied customers if you are interested call me at 927-000-000 thank you

sincerely

annie morris

SHURLEY ENGLISH

Notes: _____

_____

_____

_____

_____

_____

_____

_____

_____

_____

_____

_____

_____

_____

_____

_____

_____

_____

_____

_____

_____

_____

_____

_____

_____

_____

_____

Classroom Practice 68

Name:_____ Date:_____

PARTICIPLES

▶ **Exercise 1:** Classify the sentence. Write the participle in the first blank and the word it modifies in the second blank.

1. Those arching limbs blocked my view.
   _____ modifies _____

2. We looked for a place with running water.
   _____ modifies _____

▶ **Exercise 2:** Underline each participle once and write **P** above it. Underline each verb twice and write **V** above it.

1. We camped beside the singing waterfall.

2. The choir was singing several blues tunes.

3. The children stared at the billowing clouds.

4. The farmer studied his eroding hillside.

GERUNDS

▶ **Exercise 3:** Classify the sentence. Label each gerund with a **G** in front of the noun job.

1. Walking is my favorite pastime.

2. She enjoys painting.

▶ **Exercise 4:** Underline each gerund once and write **G** above it. Underline each verb twice and write **V** above it.

1. My mother despises lying.

2. I am flying to Florida for vacation.

3. Flying makes me nervous.

4. Shannon is not guilty of stealing.

INFINITIVES

▶ **Exercise 5:** Classify the sentence. Label each infinitive with an **I** in front of the job it performs.

1. His dream is to travel.

2. Ways to travel are few.

▶ **Exercise 6:** Underline each infinitive once and write **I** above it. Underline each verb twice and write **V** above it.

1. To sell is our best option.

2. President Lincoln loved to joke.

3. Albert wanted desperately to succeed.

4. The candidate to select should be honest.

MIXED VERBALS

▶ **Exercise 7:** Underline participles, gerunds, and infinitives once and write **P**, **G**, or **I** above them. Underline verbs twice and write **V** above them.

1. The babies went to sleep.

2. The babies are sleeping now.

3. Mindy borrowed a sleeping bag from Boris.

4. My big brother loves sleeping.

SHURLEY ENGLISH

Notes: _____

_____

_____

_____

_____

_____

_____

_____

_____

_____

_____

_____

_____

_____

_____

_____

_____

_____

_____

_____

_____

_____

_____

_____

_____

_____

_____

_____

_____

_____

Classroom Practice 69

Name:_____ Date:_____

PARTICIPLES

▶ **Exercise 1:** Classify the sentence. Write the participle in the first blank and the word it modifies in the second blank.

1. The running water ruined our bathroom floor.
_____ modifies _____

2. The falling meteor damaged two satellites.
_____ modifies _____

▶ **Exercise 2:** Underline each participle once and write **P** above it. Underline each verb twice and write **V** above it.

1. A driving snowstorm was in the forecast.

2. I imagined kites soaring.

3. Students returned to a remodeled high school.

4. A pedestrian was hit by a falling brick.

GERUNDS

▶ **Exercise 3:** Classify the sentence. Label each gerund with a **G** in front of the noun job.

1. By waiting, we bought cheaper airline tickets.

2. Digging is Thane's only bad habit.

▶ **Exercise 4:** Underline each gerund once and write **G** above it. Underline each verb twice and write **V** above it.

1. Our family enjoys camping.

2. I do not see the fun in wrestling.

3. Parallel parking is a difficult skill.

4. Dad bought tools for building.

INFINITIVES

▶ **Exercise 5:** Classify the sentence. Label each infinitive with an **I** in front of the job it performs.

1. Dad lay on the sofa to nap.

2. I needed to order from the catalog.

▶ **Exercise 6:** Underline each infinitive once and write **I** above it. Underline each verb twice and write **V** above it.

1. To win is our team's goal.

2. The pioneers wanted to farm and to hunt.

3. Betsy chose the best chocolate to buy.

4. You need to listen more carefully.

MIXED VERBALS

▶ **Exercise 7:** Underline participles, gerunds and infinitives once and write **P**, **G**, or **I** above them. Underline verbs twice and write **V** above them.

1. Resting helped the weary hikers.

2. Coach offered an encouraging word to our team.

3. The best place to eat is the New Delhi Deli.

4. Unfortunately, my dad loves to sing.

Notes: _____

_____

_____

_____

_____

_____

_____

_____

_____

_____

_____

_____

_____

_____

_____

_____

_____

_____

_____

_____

_____

_____

_____

_____

_____

_____

_____

_____

_____

_____

Classroom Practice 70

Name:_____ Date:_____

PARTICIPLES

▶ **Exercise 1:** Classify the sentence. Write the participle in the first blank and the word it modifies in the second blank.

1. Linda adopted three abandoned horses.
_____ modifies _____

2. His job offer was very tempting.
_____ modifies _____

▶ **Exercise 2:** Underline each participle once and write **P** above it. Underline each verb twice and write **V** above it.

1. Breaking waves crashed against the sea wall.

2. The embarrassed shopper left quickly.

3. Lola came back from lunch with renewed energy.

4. The shrill buzzing noise was extremely annoying.

GERUNDS

▶ **Exercise 3:** Classify the sentence. Label each gerund with a **G** in front of the noun job.

1. Yelling will not help matters.

2. The first chore in the morning is the milking.

▶ **Exercise 4:** Underline each gerund once and write **G** above it. Underline each verb twice and write **V** above it.

1. Marian's doctor recommended exercising.

2. My brother is looking into nursing as a career.

3. Rowing takes a lot of upper body strength.

4. His summer plans include a few days of loafing.

INFINITIVES

▶ **Exercise 5:** Classify the sentence. Label each infinitive with an **I** in front of the job it performs.

1. The place to visit is Jamaica.

2. On Saturdays, Dad loves to fish.

▶ **Exercise 6:** Underline each infinitive once and write **I** above it. Underline each verb twice and write **V** above it.

1. To graduate, Jonathan studied hard.

2. The cashier did not want to argue.

3. To resign will not be easy for me.

4. Few soldiers wanted to surrender.

MIXED VERBALS

▶ **Exercise 7:** Underline participles, gerunds, and infinitives once and write **P**, **G**, or **I** above them. Underline verbs twice and write **V** above them.

1. To parachute was the young man's dream.

2. James bought building materials for the project.

3. Melinda had a gentle way of speaking.

4. Jan took a class in rock climbing last summer.

SHURLEY ENGLISH

Notes: _____

_____

_____

_____

_____

_____

_____

_____

_____

_____

_____

_____

_____

_____

_____

_____

_____

_____

_____

_____

_____

_____

_____

_____

_____

_____

Classroom Practice 71, Part A

Name:_____ Date:_____

PARTICIPLES

▶ **Exercise 1:** Classify the sentence. Write the participle in the first blank and the word it modifies in the second blank.

1. The sailing ships looked beautiful in the harbor.
_____ modifies _____

2. Zach borrowed surfing equipment from David.
_____ modifies _____

▶ **Exercise 2:** Underline each participle once and write **P** above it. Underline each verb twice and write **V** above it.

1. The roaring campfire warmed the hikers.

3. Mom's waxed floors shone like glass.

2. A starving kitten lapped up the warmed milk.

4. The laughing audience whistled and applauded.

GERUNDS

▶ **Exercise 3:** Classify the sentence. Label each gerund with a **G** in front of the noun job.

1. Sailing was Uncle Russel's passion.

2. For wrapping, Simon used tissue paper.

▶ **Exercise 4:** Underline each gerund once and write **G** above it. Underline each verb twice and write **V** above it.

1. The last event will be the diving.

3. Rowing keeps Katrina in good shape.

2. We will continue talking later.

4. In public speaking, you need a pleasant voice.

INFINITIVES

▶ **Exercise 5:** Classify the sentence. Label each infinitive with an **I** in front of the job it performs.

1. Rooms to rent are listed in the classified ads.

2. The truck driver could not see to pass.

▶ **Exercise 6:** Underline each infinitive once and write **I** above it. Underline each verb twice and write **V** above it.

1. Riley decided at the last minute to go.

3. Stephen has found the best instrument to play.

2. For work, the best option was to carpool.

4. To begin, Edward read the introduction.

MIXED VERBALS

▶ **Exercise 7:** Underline participles, gerunds, and infinitives once and write **P**, **G**, or **I** above them. Underline verbs twice and write **V** above them.

1. The skydiving club meets in an abandoned airport.

3. Traveling has been a wonderful experience.

2. John went home early to pack.

4. Tyler is sweeping the broken glass.

SHURLEY ENGLISH

Classroom Practice 71, Part B

Name:_____ Date:_____

SPECIAL USAGE PROBLEMS

▶ **Exercise 8:** Underline the correct verb choice in each sentence below. Write **DO** if the verb has a direct object and **No DO** if it doesn't.

1. Mother (set, sat) the casserole dish on the kitchen counter. _____
2. Sparkling crystal pieces (set, sat) in the display cases at the gift shop. _____
3. My sick brother has (lain, laid) in the bed for three days. _____
4. My brother has (lain, laid) a huge pile of old clothes on his bed. _____
5. The sun is (raising, rising) in the eastern sky. _____
6. The construction crane is (raising, rising) the huge steel beam to the top of the skyscraper. _____

▶ **Exercise 9:** Underline the correct adjective or adverb choice in each sentence below. Write **Adj** or **Adv** and the word it modifies in the blanks at the end.

1. Georgia played (good, well) in today's match. _____ _____
2. The seventh grade students did (good, well) on their final exams. _____ _____
3. Thankfully, Grandmother is very (good, well) today. _____ _____
4. Danielle was (sure, surely) she had closed and locked the gate. _____ _____
5. (Sure, Surely), we have saved enough money for our trip. _____ _____
6. Edward and his sister were (real, really) musicians. _____ _____
7. We (real, really) enjoyed our visits to the aquarium and the zoo. _____ _____
8. The mechanic did a (bad, badly) job of repairing the transmission in my car. _____ _____
9. The contestant sang (bad, badly). _____ _____

▶ **Exercise 10:** Underline the correct word choice in each sentence below. In the blank, write **N** for noun or **V** for verb to tell how the word is used in the sentence.

1. The (affects, effects) of listening to loud music for many years had damaged his hearing. _____
2. The tempting smell of chocolate cake (affected, effected) the resolve of the dieters. _____
3. Shawn was hospitalized due to the harmful (affects, effects) of the smoke from the burning building. _____
4. The actor's engaging personality (affected, effected) the behavior of his fans. _____
5. Our principal (affected, effected) many positive changes in the morale at our school. _____

▶ **Exercise 11:** Underline the correct word choice in each sentence below.

1. Rachel and Brian have already (did, done) their daily chores, so they can watch TV.
2. Our cousins and their children have (gone, went) on vacation to Lake Nimrod in Arkansas.
3. Elaine has (come, came) to this area for a visit during her summer break from college.
4. The hikers (seen, saw) lots of wildlife on the lower trail that goes around the lake.
5. The cousins (did, done) a great job of organizing a family reunion for the Morris clan.

Classroom Practice 72

Name:_____ Date:_____

VERBALS

▶ **Exercise 1:** Underline each participle once and write **P** above it. Underline each verb twice and write **V** above it.

1. We took pictures of several carved totem poles.

2. Rolled clothing takes less space in my suitcase.

▶ **Exercise 2:** Underline each gerund once and write **G** above it. Underline each verb twice and write **V** above it.

1. My aunts enjoy walking in the mornings.

2. Revise the sentences in your writing.

▶ **Exercise 3:** Underline each infinitive once and write **I** above it. Underline each verb twice and write **V** above it.

1. We had not planned to detour on our trip.

2. To qualify, you must be at least ten years old.

▶ **Exercise 4:** Underline participles, gerunds, and infinitives once and write **P**, **G**, or **I** above them. Underline verbs twice and write **V** above them.

1. Clancy ate the burnt toast anyway.

3. Gargling is the best way to cure a sore throat.

2. To climb, you must wear special boots.

4. The farmer planted seeds in fertilized soil.

SPECIAL USAGE PROBLEMS

▶ **Exercise 5:** Underline the correct verb choice in each sentence below. Write **DO** if the verb has a direct object and **No DO** if it doesn't.

1. Please (set, sit) the cartons of ice cream in the freezer. _____

2. My cat (lay, laid) in my lap for an hour. _____

3. Our hens (lay, laid) eggs in abundance. _____

▶ **Exercise 6:** Underline the correct adjective or adverb choice in each sentence below. Write **Adj** or **Adv** and the word it modifies in the blanks at the end.

1. Jane's teachers always spoke (good, well) of her. _____ _____

2. The girl felt (bad, badly) about the way she had teased her sister. _____ _____

3. Winning the contest is not a (sure, surely) thing. _____ _____

4. I had a (real, really) great time on vacation. _____ _____

▶ **Exercise 7:** Underline the correct word choice in each sentence below. In the blank, write **N** for noun or **V** for verb to tell how the word is used in the sentence.

1. The angry crowd (affected, effected) the store owners. _____

2. The grumpy toddler finally fell asleep from the (affects, effects) of the soothing music. _____

▶ **Exercise 8:** Underline the correct verb choice in each sentence below.

1. You (was, were) a great help to us during our clean-up efforts after the tornado.

2. My friends and he have (gone, went) on an excursion to the Smoky Mountains.

3. Justin has not (did, done) his science project correctly.

4. The firefighters (seen, saw) wildfires spreading over the entire valley.

5. Why has he (come, came) to the committee meeting unprepared?

Notes: _____

_____

_____

_____

_____

_____

_____

_____

_____

_____

_____

_____

_____

_____

_____

_____

_____

_____

_____

_____

_____

_____

_____

_____

_____

_____

_____

_____

_____

_____

_____

_____

Chapter 24 Checkup 73

Name:_____ Date:_____

VERBALS

▶ **Exercise 1:** Underline each participle once and write **P** above it. Underline each verb twice and write **V** above it.

1. Faded curtains hang in her east window.   2. The storm littered the highway with broken limbs.

▶ **Exercise 2:** Underline each gerund once and write **G** above it. Underline each verb twice and write **V** above it.

1. In Switzerland, skiing is the national pastime.   2. Sometimes, walking hurts my feet.

▶ **Exercise 3:** Underline each infinitive once and write **I** above it. Underline each verb twice and write **V** above it.

1. To sit can become very tiring.   2. The boys went to the creek to fish.

▶ **Exercise 4:** Underline participles, gerunds, and infinitives once and write **P**, **G**, or **I** above them. Underline verbs twice and write **V** above them.

1. I had two messages on my answering machine.   3. Dana bought a new set of cooking utensils.

2. By calling, we were permitted to order quicker.   4. Joel went skydiving on Saturday.

SPECIAL USAGE PROBLEMS

▶ **Exercise 5:** Underline the correct verb choice in each sentence below. Write **DO** if the verb has a direct object and **No DO** if it doesn't.

1. Decorative vases were (setting, sitting) on each side of our front door. _____

2. Mother is (laying, lying) down because she has a headache. _____

3. Mary Anne is (laying, lying) the folded clothes on your bed. _____

▶ **Exercise 6:** Underline the correct adjective or adverb choice in each sentence below. Write **Adj** or **Adv** and the word it modifies in the blanks at the end.

1. Several of the young artists created (good, well) pieces for the art show. _____ _____

2. Charlotte has (sure, surely) finished cleaning her room by now. _____ _____

3. Elizabeth drove (bad, badly) during her driving test; therefore, she failed. _____ _____

▶ **Exercise 7:** Underline the correct word choice in each sentence below. In the blank, write **N** for noun or **V** for verb to tell how the word is used in the sentence.

1. One (affect, effect) of the volcanic eruption was the ash that covered everything. _____

2. The aroma of the steaks cooking on the grill (affected, effected) our dogs. _____

▶ **Exercise 8:** Underline the correct verb choice in each sentence below.

1. The gymnastics teams (did, done) several routines at their regional competition.

2. Several medical doctors from the University Hospital have (gone, went) to a diabetes seminar in Seattle.

3. The tourists (seen, saw) several wild animals while they were on a safari in Africa.

SHURLEY ENGLISH

Notes: _____

Classroom Practice 74

Name:_____ Date:_____

PARTICIPIAL PHRASES

▶ **Exercise 1:** Underline the participial phrase and write **P** in the blank.

1. Swimmers sunbathing on the beach were relaxed._____

2. The man riding the elevator was very quiet._____

3. The crew fixing potholes worked late. _____

4. I saw a man holding a sign at the airport. _____

GERUND PHRASES

▶ **Exercise 2:** Underline the gerund phrase and write **G** in the blank.

1. Bathing my black Lab is a terrible chore. _____

2. The possibility of turning back is over. _____

3. Beth enjoyed shopping for a dress. _____

4. Cutting the grass made a difference. _____

▶ **Exercise 3:** Underline the verbal phrases and identify each one with an abbreviation and function. Gerund Phrase: **GSN, GDO, GOP, GPrN,** or **GOCN.**

1. Watching the snowflakes made me homesick.

2. Her family liked gathering around the piano.

3. Molly's job is directing the traffic by the school.

4. By leaving on Friday, he saved money on his ticket.

INFINITIVE PHRASES

▶ **Exercise 4:** Underline the infinitive phrase and write **I** in the blank.

1. To act before an audience requires courage. _____

2. The captain told them to abandon the ship. _____

3. Jane's job is to lead the music. _____

4. Ruth wanted to shop at the antique mall. _____

▶ **Exercise 5:** Underline the verbal phrases and identify each one with an abbreviation and function. Infinitives: **IAdj, IAdv, ISN, IDO** or **IPrN.**

1. Regina likes to ride the merry-go-round.

2. To motivate the students is a challenge.

3. He went to the kitchen to stir the vegetables.

4. Our plan to surprise Tina has been discovered.

MIXED VERBAL PHRASES

▶ **Exercise 6:** Underline the verbal phrase in each sentence. In the blank at the end of each sentence, write **P** for a Participial Phrase, **G** for a Gerund Phrase, or **I** for an Infinitive Phrase.

1. Dresses stored in the trunk smelled of cedar. _____

2. Our business is to serve the customers. _____

3. The worst chore is cleaning the bathroom. _____

4. Our plan was to go to the movie. _____

▶ **Exercise 7:** Underline the verbal phrases and identify each one with an abbreviation and function. Participial phrase: **PAdj.** Gerund phrase: **GSN, GDO, GOP, GPrN,** or **GOCN.** Infinitive phrase: **IAdj, IAdv, ISN, IDO,** or **IPrN.**

1. To tell a lie may result in going to jail.

2. Participating in the race boosted my confidence.

3. The man carrying the camera works for the newspaper.

4. They went to the village to shop for souvenirs.

Notes: _____

Classroom Practice 75

Name:_____ Date:_____

DANGLING AND MISPLACED MODIFIERS

▶ **Exercise 1:** At the end of each sentence, write **C** if the sentence is correct, write **MM** if the sentence contains a misplaced modifier, and write **DM** if the sentence contains a dangling modifier.

1. Jeremy gave sugar cookies to his friends with sprinkles on them. _____

2. The elderly woman told me about her surgery in the seat next to me. _____

3. With great anticipation, the audience watched the daring performers. _____

4. The construction worker wearing the blue hard hat bellowed at the crane operator. _____

5. After grading the papers, the telephone rang. _____

▶ **Exercise 2:** Rewrite the sentence, correcting the *misplaced modifier*.

A young girl was walking a dog in a long black dress.

_____

_____

▶ **Exercise 3:** Rewrite the sentence, correcting the *dangling modifier*.

While cleaning out the basement, a raccoon appeared from behind one of the boxes.

_____

_____

VERBAL PHRASES

▶ **Exercise 4:** Underline the verbal phrase in each sentence. In the blank at the end of each sentence, write **P** for a Participial Phrase, **G** for a Gerund Phrase, or **I** for an Infinitive Phrase.

1. My son likes to paint with watercolors. _____

2. Vanessa prefers eating at a deli. _____

3. Dan always enjoys fishing in tournaments. _____

4. She stared at the girl doing her homework. _____

5. I talked to the two boys playing marbles. _____

6. Shannon is wanting to place an order. _____

7. Doing crossword puzzles is my hobby. _____

8. Potatoes baked in an oven are quite tasty. _____

▶ **Exercise 5:** Underline the verbal phrases and identify each one with an abbreviation and function.
Participial phrase: **PAdj.** Gerund phrase: **GSN, GDO, GOP, GPrN,** or **GOCN.**
Infinitive phrase: **IAdj, IAdv, ISN, IDO,** or **IPrN.**

1. I noticed the woman wearing the red hat.

2. To step on a rusty nail is painful.

3. On Wednesdays, we like to eat at Pete's Pizza.

4. Driving in bad weather is no fun.

5. The vines growing on the fence are honeysuckle.

6. On cold nights, they enjoy sleeping by the campfire.

Notes: _____

_____

_____

_____

_____

_____

_____

_____

_____

_____

_____

_____

_____

_____

_____

_____

_____

_____

_____

_____

_____

_____

_____

_____

_____

_____

_____

_____

_____

_____

_____

Classroom Practice 76

Name:_____   Date:_____

DANGLING AND MISPLACED MODIFIERS

▶ **Exercise 1:** At the end of each sentence, write **C** if the sentence is correct, write **MM** if the sentence contains a misplaced modifier, and write **DM** if the sentence contains a dangling modifier.

1. Eating too much, my stomach was upset. _____

2. My cousin rented an apartment from a realtor with no inside plumbing. _____

3. Pamela made several beautiful costumes for the skaters with sequins on them. _____

4. Sprinting for the bus, my notebook fell in the mud. _____

5. Under the porch, Becky found her history textbook covered with mud. _____

▶ **Exercise 2:** Rewrite the sentence, correcting the *misplaced modifier*.

The young man walked toward the bus carrying a suitcase.

_____

_____

▶ **Exercise 3:** Rewrite the sentence, correcting the *dangling modifier*.

Scanning through the newspaper, an advertisement for landscaping caught my eye.

_____

_____

VERBAL PHRASES

▶ **Exercise 4:** Underline the verbal phrase in each sentence. In the blank at the end of each sentence, write **P** for a Participial Phrase, **G** for a Gerund Phrase, or **I** for an Infinitive Phrase.

1. My teacher likes to talk about dinosaurs. _____

2. The apple pie covered with cheese was delicious. _____

3. Blake hated to walk on the white carpet. _____

4. Reading mystery books is Rose's favorite pastime. _____

5. The lady washing her car is my aunt. _____

6. Scrubbing floors is a necessary chore. _____

7. Casey's dream is to become a doctor. _____

8. He thanked me for painting the fence. _____

▶ **Exercise 5:** Underline the verbal phrases and identify each one with an abbreviation and function.
Participial phrase: **PAdj**. Gerund phrase: **GSN, GDO, GOP, GPrN,** or **GOCN**.
Infinitive phrase: **IAdj, IAdv, ISN, IDO,** or **IPrN**.

1. My normal routine on Fridays is to get a hair cut.

2. We watched the snake slithering under a rock.

3. My family wants to move to Colorado.

4. The cat lying on my windowsill is asleep.

5. The football coach believes in lifting weights.

6. Chewing gum is not allowed in class.

Notes: _____

_____

_____

_____

_____

_____

_____

_____

_____

_____

_____

_____

_____

_____

_____

_____

_____

_____

_____

_____

_____

_____

_____

_____

_____

_____

_____

_____

_____

_____

Chapter 25 Checkup 77

Name:_____ Date:_____

DANGLING AND MISPLACED MODIFIERS

▶ **Exercise 1:** At the end of each sentence, write **C** if the sentence is correct, write **MM** if the sentence contains a misplaced modifier, and write **DM** if the sentence contains a dangling modifier.

1. Cynthia and Gerald saw several unusual flowers hiking across the field. _____

2. I found my missing baseball glove cleaning my room. _____

3. Forgetting to buy gas, the motorcycle wouldn't start. _____

4. Not seeing the pothole, the skateboard went flying. _____

5. While I was reading a magazine, my dog jumped into my lap. _____

▶ **Exercise 2:** Rewrite the sentence, correcting the *misplaced modifier*.

We saw several camels on vacation in Africa.

_____

_____

▶ **Exercise 3:** Rewrite the sentence, correcting the *dangling modifier*.

While trying to get ready for school, the doorbell suddenly rang.

_____

_____

VERBAL PHRASES

▶ **Exercise 4:** Underline the verbal phrase in each sentence. In the blank at the end of each sentence, write **P** for a Participial Phrase, **G** for a Gerund Phrase, or **I** for an Infinitive Phrase.

1. The carpenters building our house are professionals. _____

2. I was fascinated by the monkey grooming her baby. _____

3. Painting signs is the work of commercial artists. _____

4. Jonathan needs to borrow someone's crutches. _____

5. On hot days, Jillian likes to drink iced tea. _____

6. I usually prefer staying at home. _____

7. A family of mice tried to infest my attic. _____

8. I saw the smoke curling toward the sky. _____

▶ **Exercise 5:** Underline the verbal phrases and identify each one with an abbreviation and function.
Participial phrase: **PAdj**. Gerund phrase: **GSN, GDO, GOP, GPrN,** or **GOCN.**
Infinitive phrase: **IAdj, IAdv, ISN, IDO,** or **IPrN.**

1. The girl climbing into the saddle is a novice.

2. At the movies, I love munching on popcorn.

3. The items marked in red are not available.

4. After dinner, Mr. Bowman tried to read his mail.

5. The ladies waiting for the bus do not speak English.

6. For the Lees, flying kites is a favorite family activity.

SHURLEY ENGLISH

Notes: _____

_____

_____

_____

_____

_____

_____

_____

_____

_____

_____

_____

_____

_____

_____

_____

_____

_____

_____

_____

_____

_____

_____

_____

_____

_____

_____

_____

_____

_____

Classroom Practice 78

Name:_____ Date:_____

SKILLS

▶ **Exercise 1:** Identifying and numbering clauses
  1. Identify the independent clause and mark the subject and the verb with the numeral **1**.
  2. Identify the subordinate clause and mark the subject and the verb with the numeral **2**.
  3. Identify the word that introduces a subordinate clause and put parentheses around it.
  4. Underline the independent clause once and the subordinate clause twice.

1. Whenever I go to the library, I always find a good book.

2. We go to the lake every weekend because we like water sports.

3. The lodge where we stayed last night had a huge wood-burning fireplace.

4. She dropped her homework as she hurried after the bus.

5. The lady whose car ran out of gas was within a mile of home.

6. When Jessie and Vernon painted the hallway, they splattered paint on the carpet.

7. A friend whom I met at the park lived in an apartment nearby.

8. My friend and I were greeted by a friendly flight attendant when we boarded the plane.

▶ **Exercise 2:** Write two complex sentences. For each sentence, follow the instructions below.
  1. Identify the independent clause and mark the subject and the verb with the numeral **1**.
  2. Identify the subordinate clause and mark the subject and the verb with the numeral **2**.
  3. Identify the word that introduces a subordinate clause and put parentheses around it.
  4. Underline the independent clause once and the subordinate clause twice.

1. _____

   _____

   _____

2. _____

   _____

   _____

SHURLEY ENGLISH

Notes:

Classroom Practice 79

Name:_____ Date:_____

SKILLS

▶ **Exercise 1:** Adverb Clauses
 1. Identify the independent clause and mark the subject and the verb with the numeral **1**.
 2. Identify the subordinate clause and mark the subject and the verb with the numeral **2**.
 3. Identify the word that introduces a subordinate clause and put parentheses around it.
 4. Underline the independent clause once and the subordinate clause twice.
 5. In the first blank, write the function of the subordinate clause (**Adv**).
 6. In the second blank, write the word(s) from the independent clause that the subordinate clause modifies.
  Use these adverb questions: How? When? Where? Why? Under what condition? To what degree?

 1. Since you have been mowing all morning, I will do the rest of the yard. _____ _____

 2. He bought a new car after he wrecked his first one. _____ _____

 3. I eat steak and baked potatoes because I love them. _____ _____

 4. As he left the limousine, he smiled and waved at the crowd. _____ _____

 5. I am checking my e-mail before you get on my computer. _____ _____

 6. I have been working on my speech since you saw me last week. _____ _____

 7. Before the referee blew the whistle, the player had scored two more points. _____ _____

 8. After you begin fulltime, the job will seem less confusing. _____ _____

▶ **Exercise 2:** Each complex sentence contains an adverb clause. Underline the adverb clause. Above the clause, write the verb it modifies and the adverb question.

 1. I will grill the hamburgers while you make the potato salad.

 2. Since I have a new computer, we must e-mail each other.

 3. I broke my arm because I tripped over my brother's skate.

▶ **Exercise 3:** Write a complex sentence containing an adverb clause. Underline the adverb clause. Above the clause, write the verb it modifies and the adverb question.

_____

_____

_____

Notes: _____

_____

_____

_____

_____

_____

_____

_____

_____

_____

_____

_____

_____

_____

_____

_____

_____

_____

_____

_____

_____

_____

_____

_____

_____

_____

_____

_____

Classroom Practice 80

Name:_____ Date:_____

SKILLS

▶ **Exercise 1:** Adjective Clauses
1. Identify the independent clause and mark the subject and the verb with the numeral **1**.
2. Identify the subordinate clause and mark the subject and the verb with the numeral **2**.
3. Identify the word that introduces a subordinate clause and put parentheses around it.
4. Underline the independent clause once and the subordinate clause twice.
5. In the first blank, write the function of the subordinate clause (**Adj**).
6. In the second blank, write the word(s) from the independent clause that the subordinate clause modifies.
   Use these adjective questions: What kind? Which one?

   1. We congratulated the soccer players who won the game. _____ _____

   2. The man whose suitcase was lost at the airport searched everywhere for it. _____ _____

   3. The woman whom you helped is my mother. _____ _____

   4. I have seven little felines that especially like to annoy my guests. _____ _____

   5. We pitched our tent on a mountaintop that overlooked the valley. _____ _____

▶ **Exercise 2:** Adverb Clauses
1. Identify the independent clause and mark the subject and the verb with the numeral **1**.
2. Identify the subordinate clause and mark the subject and the verb with the numeral **2**.
3. Identify the word that introduces a subordinate clause and put parentheses around it.
4. Underline the independent clause once and the subordinate clause twice.
5. In the first blank, write the function of the subordinate clause (**Adv**).
6. In the second blank, write the word(s) from the independent clause that the subordinate clause modifies.
   Use these adverb questions: How? When? Where? Why? Under what condition? To what degree?

   1. Rose and Emma waved to us as they walked toward the bus. _____ _____

   2. After the seals perform each trick, they are fed fish for a treat. _____ _____

   3. When my grandmother fell, she broke her arm. _____ _____

▶ **Exercise 3:** Each complex sentence contains an adverb or adjective clause. Underline the adverb or adjective clause. Above the clause, write the word it modifies and the adverb or adjective question.

   1. The gymnast who is on crutches is my friend, Lucky.

   2. After the science meeting concluded, the members ate sandwiches and chips.

▶ **Exercise 4:** Write a complex sentence containing an adjective clause. Underline the adjective clause. Above the clause, write the noun or pronoun it modifies and the adjective question.

Notes: _____

_____

_____

_____

_____

_____

_____

_____

_____

_____

_____

_____

_____

_____

_____

_____

_____

_____

_____

_____

_____

_____

_____

_____

_____

_____

_____

_____

_____

_____

Classroom Practice 81

Name:_____ Date:_____

SKILLS

▶ **Exercise 1:** Mixed Adverb and Adjective Clauses
1. Identify the independent clause and mark the subject and the verb with the numeral **1**.
2. Identify the subordinate clause and mark the subject and the verb with the numeral **2**.
3. Identify the word that introduces a subordinate clause and put parentheses around it.
4. Underline the independent clause once and the subordinate clause twice.
5. In the first blank, write the function of the subordinate clause (**Adv** or **Adj**).
6. In the second blank, write the word(s) from the independent clause that the subordinate clause modifies.
   Use these adjective questions: What kind? Which one?
   Use these adverb questions: How? When? Where? Why? Under what condition? To what degree?

1. People who buy stocks do not always make money. _____ _____

2. After you have finished the examination, I will take your paper. _____ _____

3. I cried as my son accepted the award for bravery. _____ _____

4. Friends whom you have helped over the years respect and love you. _____ _____

5. Tony kept the two dogs that had belonged to his father. _____ _____

6. After Jason got his license, Aunt Hilda worried for months. _____ _____

7. Ginger returned to the country where her mother was born. _____ _____

8. The man who led his people across the mountains became a national hero. _____ _____

▶ **Exercise 2:** Each complex sentence contains an adverb or adjective clause. Underline the adverb or adjective clause. Above the clause, write the word it modifies and the adverb or adjective question.

1. The house where I grew up is at the end of this road.

2. We want to meet the benefactor who helped us through college.

▶ **Exercise 3:**
1. Write a complex sentence containing an adverb clause. Underline the adverb clause. Above the adverb clause, write the verb it modifies and the adverb question.

2. Write a complex sentence containing an adjective clause. Underline the adjective clause. Above the adjective clause, write the noun or pronoun it modifies and the adjective question.

Notes: _____

_____

_____

_____

_____

_____

_____

_____

_____

_____

_____

_____

_____

_____

_____

_____

_____

_____

_____

_____

_____

_____

_____

_____

_____

_____

Chapter 26 Checkup 82

Name:_____ Date:_____

SKILLS

▶ **Exercise 1:** Mixed Adverb and Adjective Clauses
  1. Identify the independent clause and mark the subject and the verb with the numeral **1**.
  2. Identify the subordinate clause and mark the subject and the verb with the numeral **2**.
  3. Identify the word that introduces a subordinate clause and put parentheses around it.
  4. Underline the independent clause once and the subordinate clause twice.
  5. In the first blank, write the function of the subordinate clause (**Adv** or **Adj**).
  6. In the second blank, write the word(s) from the independent clause that the subordinate clause modifies.
     Use these adjective questions: What kind? Which one?
     Use these adverb questions: How? When? Where? Why? Under what condition? To what degree?

  1. Whenever we have company, my cat gets nervous and hides. _____ _____

  2. James Michener is an author whose books are about Hawaii. _____ _____

  3. When you have time, would you like to have dinner with us? _____ _____

  4. Mom was pretty upset after we tracked mud through the house. _____ _____

  5. The car, which came with the free vacation, was a limousine. _____ _____

  6. We honored the veterans that fought in World War II. _____ _____

  7. Because Mattie went to Canada, she did not work at the YWCA this summer. _____ _____

  8. They were led into the forest by a leprechaun who was only six inches tall. _____ _____

▶ **Exercise 2:** Each complex sentence contains an adverb or adjective clause. Underline the adverb or adjective clause. Above the clause, write the word it modifies and the adverb or adjective question.

  1. The scientist whom I met at the airport was from Germany.

  2. When the sun went down, fog settled in the valley.

▶ **Exercise 3:**
  1. Write a complex sentence containing an adverb clause. Underline the adverb clause. Above the adverb clause, write the verb it modifies and the adverb question.

  2. Write a complex sentence containing an adjective clause. Underline the adjective clause. Above the adjective clause, write the noun or pronoun it modifies and the adjective question.

Notes: _____

_____

_____

_____

_____

_____

_____

_____

_____

_____

_____

_____

_____

_____

_____

_____

_____

_____

_____

_____

_____

_____

_____

_____

_____

_____

_____

_____

Classroom Practice 83

Name:_____ Date:_____

SKILLS

Exercise 1: Noun Clauses
1. Identify the independent clause and mark the subject and the verb with the numeral **1**.
2. Identify the subordinate clause and mark the subject and the verb with the numeral **2**.
3. Identify the word that introduces a subordinate clause and put parentheses around it.
4. Underline the independent clause once and the subordinate clause twice.
5. In the blank, write the function of the noun clause (**SN, OP, DO, IO, PrN**). Draw a box around the noun clause used as a subject. Then, draw a box around the numeral 1 that identifies the noun clause as the subject.

1. I believe that it is snowing. _____

2. Bruce loaned the DVD to whoever wanted it. _____

3. The principal awarded whoever participated a ribbon. _____

4. Eggs and bacon are what I ate for breakfast. _____

5. That the television is too loud is very apparent. _____

Exercise 2: Follow the directions given in Exercise 1.

1. Benjamin and Valerie are who I consider my best friends. _____

2. Mother handed out cold tablets to whoever was there. _____

3. That he is very talented is evident. _____

4. Melissa could not see where she was driving. _____

5. The supervisor gave whoever worked the late shift a bonus. _____

Exercise 3: Write a complex sentence with a noun clause of your choice. Label your sentence, using the directions in Exercise 1.

_____

_____

_____

SHURLEY ENGLISH

Notes: _____

_____

_____

_____

_____

_____

_____

_____

_____

_____

_____

_____

_____

_____

_____

_____

_____

_____

_____

_____

_____

_____

_____

_____

_____

_____

_____

Classroom Practice 84

Name:_____ Date:_____

SKILLS

Exercise 1: Noun Clauses

1. Identify the independent clause and mark the subject and the verb with the numeral **1**.
2. Identify the subordinate clause and mark the subject and the verb with the numeral **2**.
3. Identify the word that introduces a subordinate clause and put parentheses around it.
4. Underline the independent clause once and the subordinate clause twice.
5. In the blank, write the function of the noun clause (**SN, OP, DO, IO, PrN**). Draw a box around the noun clause used as a subject. Then, draw a box around the numeral 1 that identifies the noun clause as the subject.

1. I just learned that you came after all. _____

2. Virginia will talk to whoever is in charge. _____

3. What the man saw helped solve the crime. _____

4. I thought that you were going home early. _____

5. She played her mandolin for whoever would listen. _____

6. My brother sent whoever was in the limousine a secret message. _____

7. Coach knows why you quit the team. _____

8. New shoes are what I purchased from the store. _____

9. We gave the flyers to whoever would read them. _____

Exercise 2: Write a complex sentence with a noun clause of your choice. Label your sentence, using the directions in Exercise 1.

_____

_____

_____

Notes: _____

Classroom Practice 85

Name:_____ Date:_____

SKILLS

Exercise 1: Mixed Adverb, Adjective, and Noun Clauses
1. Identify the independent clause and mark the subject and the verb with the numeral **1**.
2. Identify the subordinate clause and mark the subject and the verb with the numeral **2**.
3. Identify the word that introduces a subordinate clause and put parentheses around it.
4. Underline the independent clause once and the subordinate clause twice.
5. If it is an adverb or adjective clause, write the function of the subordinate clause (**Adv** or **Adj**) in the blank.
6. If it is a noun clause, write the function of the noun clause in the blank (**SN, OP, DO, IO, PrN**). Draw a box around the noun clause used as a subject. Then, draw a box around the numeral 1 that identifies the noun clause as the subject.

1. When the recess bell rang, Jay fell out of his seat. _____

2. The little boy hugged the woman who saved his mother's life. _____

3. I gave the tickets to whoever was at the desk. _____

4. Will you tell us how you finally solved the puzzle? _____

5. Gina told whoever would listen her vacation plans. _____

6. My guess is that your parents will be happy. _____

7. How you can tell such a funny joke is a mystery to me. _____

Exercise 2: 1. Write a complex sentence with an adverb clause. Label your sentence, using the directions in Exercise 1.
2. Write a complex sentence with an adjective clause. Label your sentence, using the directions in Exercise 1.
3. Write a complex sentence with a noun clause. Label your sentence, using the directions in Exercise 1.

1. _____

_____

_____

2. _____

_____

_____

3. _____

_____

_____

Notes: _____

_____

_____

_____

_____

_____

_____

_____

_____

_____

_____

_____

_____

_____

_____

_____

_____

_____

_____

_____

_____

_____

_____

_____

_____

_____

_____

_____

_____

_____

Classroom Practice 86

Name:_____ Date:_____

SKILLS

Exercise 1: Underline the subordinate clause. Identify each subordinate clause as essential (**E**) or nonessential (**NE**). Set off nonessential clauses with commas.

1. Robert Parker whose father is a doctor plans to study medicine. _____

2. My friend has written a book which he wants to publish. _____

3. The trees that I planted yesterday are doing quite well. _____

4. My pet bird that is in a cage in my bedroom talks to me constantly. _____

Exercise 2: Mixed Adverb, Adjective, and Noun Clauses
1. Identify the independent clause and mark the subject and the verb with the numeral **1**.
2. Identify the subordinate clause and mark the subject and the verb with the numeral **2**.
3. Identify the word that introduces a subordinate clause and put parentheses around it.
4. Underline the independent clause once and the subordinate clause twice.
5. If it is an adverb or adjective clause, write the function of the subordinate clause (**Adv** or **Adj**) in the blank.
6. If it is a noun clause, write the function of the noun clause in the blank (**SN, OP, DO, IO, PrN**). Draw a box around the noun clause used as a subject. Then, draw a box around the numeral 1 that identifies the noun clause as the subject.

1. The secretary will give the wallet to whoever claims it. _____

2. The shepherd believed that his sheep were safe. _____

3. The judges will award whoever has the most original story a prize. _____

4. My dream is that I will become a famous writer. _____

5. That you are still alive is a miracle! _____

6. He gets hiccups if he eats too fast. _____

7. My dog bit the man who reads my water meter. _____

Exercise 3: 1. Write a complex sentence with an adverb clause. Label your sentence, using the directions in Exercise 1.
2. Write a complex sentence with an adjective clause. Label your sentence, using the directions in Exercise 1.
3. Write a complex sentence with a noun clause. Label your sentence, using the directions in Exercise 1.

1. _____
_____
_____

2. _____
_____
_____

3. _____
_____

Notes:

Chapter 27 Checkup 87

Name:_____ Date:_____

SKILLS

Exercise 1: Underline the subordinate clause. Identify each subordinate clause as essential (**E**) or nonessential (**NE**). Set off nonessential clauses with commas.

1. My little Pomeranian chased the squirrel that is a real pest. _____

2. Our neighbor's cows which are Holsteins head toward the milk barn at exactly 4:00 every day. _____

3. Students who are trying out for the basketball team should meet in the gym after school. _____

4. The historical hotel in our town which was built in 1900 is being renovated next week. _____

Exercise 2: Mixed Adverb, Adjective, and Noun Clauses
1. Identify the independent clause and mark the subject and the verb with the numeral **1**.
2. Identify the subordinate clause and mark the subject and the verb with the numeral **2**.
3. Identify the word that introduces a subordinate clause and put parentheses around it.
4. Underline the independent clause once and the subordinate clause twice.
5. If it is an adverb or adjective clause, write the function of the subordinate clause (**Adv** or **Adj**) in the blank.
6. If it is a noun clause, write the function of the noun clause in the blank (**SN, OP, DO, IO, PrN**). Draw a box around the noun clause used as a subject. Then, draw a box around the numeral 1 that identifies the noun clause as the subject.

1. Wilma will give whoever wants one a free pass. _____

2. Another course in math is what my counselor recommended. _____

3. Whoever tracks my waxed floors will be in big trouble. _____

4. He seldom knows what he is doing. _____

5. I will listen carefully to whatever you propose. _____

6. The phone rings whenever I sit down to eat. _____

7. The day before I flew to Japan was a miserably humid day. _____

Exercise 3: 1. Write a complex sentence with an adverb clause. Label your sentence, using the directions in Exercise 1.
2. Write a complex sentence with an adjective clause. Label your sentence, using the directions in Exercise 1.
3. Write a complex sentence with a noun clause. Label your sentence, using the directions in Exercise 1.

1. _____
_____
_____

2. _____
_____
_____

3. _____
_____
_____

Notes: _____

_____

_____

_____

_____

_____

_____

_____

_____

_____

_____

_____

_____

_____

_____

_____

_____

_____

_____

_____

_____

_____

_____

_____

_____

_____

_____

_____

_____

Classroom Practice 88

Name:_____ Date:_____

SKILLS

▶ **Exercise 1:** For each statement, write **O** (opinion) or **F** (fact) in the blank.

_____ 1. You will need a birth certificate to get your passport.

_____ 2. You will need to either sail or fly to England.

_____ 3. The blood in the human body has red blood cells and white blood cells.

_____ 4. Too much television-watching causes stupidity.

_____ 5. You can't buy a better car for the money.

_____ 6. If it rains again, someone is going to get hurt on that road.

▶ **Exercise 2:** Use these abbreviations to indicate the following propaganda techniques: **L** (loaded words), **I** (important/famous people), **B** (bandwagon), **M** (mudslinging), **S** (stereotyping), **F/O** (fact/opinion)

_____ 1. This electrical unit has been tested in snow, wind, ice, heat, and rain. It will last you a life-time.

_____ 2. Come to the fund raiser tonight. Everyone will be there.

_____ 3. I live in a neighborhood with big houses because I want good neighbors.

_____ 4. If you want to keep your youthful smile and have healthy teeth, use Dr. Toothy toothbrushes.

_____ 5. Most of the stars of that show use Radiant makeup products.

_____ 6. How can we expect our children to be honest when our governor acts like a common criminal?

▶ **Exercise 3:** Write True or False before each statement.

_____ 1. A fact is often followed by an opinion.

_____ 2. Although an opinion might be true, it has not been proven true.

_____ 3. If enough people believe an opinion, it is probably safe to believe it is true.

_____ 4. If you understand how propaganda works, you are less likely to fall victim to it.

_____ 5. Words such as *hope, seem, best, think,* etc. identify truthful statements.

_____ 6. Propaganda is an effort to change the opinions and actions of people.

_____ 7. Mudslinging avoids important issues by attacking an individual instead of the issue.

▶ **Exercise 4:** Answer the questions below, using the information in the following article.

(1) A Megatown Superstore will bring good jobs to the community of Pettyville, just as it did with your neighboring towns. **(2)** In the last three years, we have built a dozen Megatowns in your state; no one else has done as much for local communities. **(3)** The neglected state of your historic downtown will be improved by a glittering, new store. **(4)** The thoughtless individuals working against rezoning don't care about the crime and disease potential that goes hand-in-hand with old houses and neighborhoods. **(5)** Everyone who cares about your community will support the rezoning. **(6)** Sign the petition to rezone Pettyville; your mayor supports this change as do the business and religious leaders of your community.

By "Big Jim" McPherson, CEO of Megatown Superstore Corporation

1. Who wrote this information? _____

_____

2. What is the purpose? _____

_____

3. Write the propaganda technique used for each numbered sentence above.

(1) _____   (4) _____

(2) _____   (5) _____

(3) _____   (6) _____

Notes: _____

Classroom Practice 89

Name:_____ Date:_____

SKILLS

▶ **Exercise 1:** For each statement, write **O** (opinion) or **F** (fact) in the blank.

_____ 1. Skybird Airlines has more intercontinental flights than any other airline.

_____ 2. Skybird's pilots have more hours in the air than any other aviators in the United States.

_____ 3. Skybird's staff is the best trained and most dedicated in the world.

_____ 4. Our rainfall level is six inches short of last year's total at this time.

_____ 5. Volunteer water conservation will alleviate the water-shortage problems soon.

▶ **Exercise 2:** Use these abbreviations to indicate the following propaganda techniques: **L** (loaded words), **I** (important/famous people), **B** (bandwagon), **M** (mudslinging), **S** (stereotyping), **F/O** (fact/opinion)

_____ 1. He has $2.6 million to spend on his campaign; he'll double that by the end of the year.

_____ 2. Most students your age already own one of VirtualTalk's new cell phones.

_____ 3. Trust him if you want, but I've heard that his family has ties with organized crime.

_____ 4. It's OK to smoke; I've seen pictures of American presidents smoking cigars.

_____ 5. The families that live on Round Mountain don't care about progress the way we do.

_____ 6. You will live a healthier life in Vermont; it has green mountains, no stress, and clean air.

▶ **Exercise 3:** Write True or False before each statement.

_____ 1. Words such as *believe, feel, should,* etc. are used to introduce factual statements.

_____ 2. An effective way to spread propaganda is through mass media.

_____ 3. If a message is broadcast via reputable mass media, you can be certain that it is fact and not opinion.

_____ 4. A factual statement is often paired with a statement of opinion.

_____ 5. People very often do not know that the media is feeding them propaganda.

▶ **Exercise 4:** Answer the questions below, using the information in the following advertisement.

(1) Good people, please contribute to our righteous cause. **(2)** The clergy of your local Baptist and Catholic churches, as well as the rabbi of the synagogue, have privately contributed to our organization. **(3)** Last year, we received in excess of 4 million dollars in contributions; our mission has changed the lives of more people than any other charitable organization ever. **(4)** Don't assume that your government can do the job; we know how money in the hands of government bureaucrats is usually squandered. **(5)** Furthermore, most elected officials cannot be trusted to help the homeless and the poor. **(6)** It is up to us, ordinary people like you and me, to solve these problems.

1. What is the purpose? _____

2. Write the propaganda technique for each numbered sentence above.

(1) _____   (4) _____

(2) _____   (5) _____

(3) _____   (6) _____

SHURLEY ENGLISH

Notes: